She spun round, and the ___ the corridor watching he___ much?' he enquired mila___.

Caroline was silent, surprised to find that she was not in the least afraid of him, but was simply nonplussed.

'The trouble is,' she said, 'I just don't know what to believe. You warned me that I might put myself into danger by prying into your affairs . . .'

'I did nothing of the sort! I warned you against taking too much interest in the smugglers! I said nothing about my own concerns.'

'But I thought . . . Oh.' Caroline suddenly realised that this was quite true.

'It seems to me,' he observed judicially, 'that you've been letting your imagination run away with you. I'll admit that, at first glance, my behaviour is a little suspicious—sudden comings and goings, odd visitors at strange hours, no social chit-chat about where I've been or what I've been doing, but I've explained all that to you. Why do you still think I'm up to some sort of villainy?'

Why indeed, thought Caroline, did she harbour such ridiculous and suspicions about a man with whom she was almost prepared to admit that she was in love . . .

Dinah Dean was born in Northamptonshire, but she has lived for most of her life in the Home Counties. She was a teacher until 1979, when she decided to give more time to her writing, and since then has fitted it in 'around local history studies, reading and conversation, well-seasoned with trips abroad, preferably to Scandinavia and Russia.' She lives in Waltham Abbey in Essex which, in some respects, bears a strong resemblance to the fictional Woodham, which first featured in her last novel, *The Country Gentleman*.

The Country Cousins is her eighth Masquerade Historical Romance.

THE COUNTRY COUSINS

DINAH DEAN

MILLS & BOON LIMITED
15–16 BROOK'S NEWS
LONDON W1A 1DR

First published in Great Britain 1986
by Mills & Boon Limited

© Dinah Dean 1986

Australian copyright 1986
Philippine copyright 1986

ISBN 0 263 75423 5

Set in 10 on 11 pt Linotron Times
04-0686-74,600

Photoset by Rowland Phototypesetting Limited
Bury St Edmunds, Suffolk
Made and printed in Great Britain by
Cox & Wyman Limited, Reading

For Liz, Al and Thomas

CHAPTER
ONE

IT WAS unfortunate that Mr Hartwell chose to call on the fourth of September, for anyone in Stepney could have told him that Mrs Barnes had her wash-day on the first Monday in every month, and, being the thrifty wife of a City merchant, she chose to conduct such household matters herself.

Mr Hartwell, on the other hand, was of the Landed Gentry, and left the running of his residence to his housekeeper, so he arrived in all innocence at the pleasant house near St Dunstan's church in his smart town carriage, and sent his groom to mount the four steps to the white door in the centre of the double-fronted brick house, pull the gleaming brass bell-knob, and hand in his master's card with a polite request that Mrs Barnes should spare him a few minutes of her time.

The footman, who had been cleaning the silver in his shirt-sleeves and had been obliged to don his morning livery coat in some haste, pulling white gloves over his plate-powdered hands, raised his eyebrows in a superior fashion at the groom, regarded the carriage with rather more respect, and, saying he would 'henquire', closed the door and retired into the back regions, where he found the mistress in the large wash-house, pensively prodding with a dolly-stick at the sheets boiling in the copper, a large apron protecting her fashionable poplin morning dress.

She took the proffered card, read the name, thought for a moment, and then, looking slightly vexed, instructed the footman to admit the gentleman to the parlour. She cast a sharp eye on the three laundry-women, the maids, and her two daughters, who had all paused in their various tasks out of curiosity over this unwonted interruption.

'Come with me, Caroline,' she instructed her elder daughter, 'and the rest of you carry on with your work. Don't forget, Alice'—this to her younger daughter—'that the lace is to be washed in milk. Your father did not pay the exorbitant price asked for that collar for you to ruin it at the first wash! I really don't know,' she continued as she took off her apron and shooed Caroline before her into the kitchen, 'why fashion decrees French lace when we're at war with them, and English lace is every bit as good. Tidy yourself, girl! I've no wish for you to look like a tradesman's daughter to this—this person!'

Caroline thought with some amusement that she was, in fact, a tradesman's daughter, for her father was a prosperous merchant in the East India trade, but she kept the thought to herself, took off her own apron, shook out her sprigged muslin frock, and, looking in the rather patchy mirror on the back of the kitchen door, tweaked her dark curls, which were already quite tidy, and wished once more that she might be allowed to have her hair cut short, for she was sure the style would suit her.

'Did not James say that the gentleman wishes to speak to you, Mama?' she asked, wondering who could be so important that both her mother and herself, the first lieutenant, should be obliged by his arrival to leave the wash-house.

'I have no wish to see Mr Hartwell at all,' Mrs Barnes replied. 'But since he is here, I suppose I must do so, but only in the presence of a third party. You need not speak, but listen carefully to everything he says.'

With that, she set her lips in a tight and unforthcoming

line, tied the strings of her clean cap with a jerk, and set sail for the parlour, her daughter following like a frigate behind a man o' war.

Mr Hartwell was standing by the window, apparently looking across to the still-countrified churchyard of St Dunstan's, but he turned as Mrs Barnes and Caroline entered, and advanced to meet them, speaking in a pleasant tone, despite the forbidding glower on the elder lady's face.

'Good morning, ma'am. It's most kind of you to receive me.'

'Yes,' Mrs Barnes replied non-committally, seating herself imperiously on one of her new sabre-legged chairs and motioning to Caroline to sit unobtrusively by the door. 'What do you want?'

Caroline was puzzled. It was not at all like her mother to be so brusque—rude, indeed—and the gentleman standing in the middle of the room seemed to have done nothing to deserve such treatment. He was quite tall, slimly built, dressed in a fashion which did credit both to his taste and his tailor in a dark blue coat and nankeen trousers of excellent cut and fit. His linen was pristinely clean and well starched, his brown hair well cut and brushed, and the only fault she herself could see in him was a somewhat arrogant tilt to his head and a touch of hauteur about his features, which were otherwise reasonably handsome. She awaited his reply with interest.

'First, to make my apologies for not making contact with you much earlier,' he replied equably, 'but I was not even aware of your existence until a few days ago.'

Mrs Barnes made no reply, and looked, if anything, more hostile.

'Second,' he continued after a slight pause, 'to bring you, I'm afraid, unhappy news about your sister.'

'If you mean Maria Hartwell,' Mrs Barnes replied, 'you must understand that she disowned me more than twenty years ago. The feeling was mutual.' Her lips closed at the end of this brief but remarkable speech with a snap which was almost audible.

'So I collect from the information concerning you which I received at the end of last week.' Mr Hartwell seemed, on the whole, unperturbed by her hostility, but he abandoned his somewhat tentative approach and went on in a brisk and business-like fashion, 'Your sister, ma'am, is my father's second wife, and my step-mother. She and my father took advantage of the Peace of Amiens in '02 to travel to France, leaving my elder half-sister in the care of her godmother, Lady Stavely, and taking their younger daughter with them. Unfortunately, they were still in France when hostilities were resumed the following year, and have been prisoners ever since.'

There was a brief pause, and then Mrs Barnes said coldly, 'How unfortunate for Lord Hartwell and the child! I am very sorry to hear of this, for I pity anyone put into the power of Bonaparte for six years!'

'And your sister, ma'am!'

'Your stepmother is well able to take care of herself. Is that all you wished to tell me? If so, I thank you for your well-meaning intentions, and bid you good day.'

With that, Mrs Barnes rose to her feet, but Mr Hartwell, uncowed by her abruptness, replied smoothly, 'No, ma'am! It is not all. By your leave . . .'

Mrs Barnes hesitated for a moment, then, to her daughter's surprise, sat down again. Caroline was familiar with the decisive note in her mother's voice during her last speech, and had not expected her to relent in the least—this was quite unprecedented! In fact, the whole episode was amazing, for, until this morning, Caroline had been quite unaware that her mother even had a sister, let alone one married to a Lord—a Baron, presumably, as the son was a plain Mister.

'As you wish,' Mrs Barnes said, still sounding disagreeable.

'I am very concerned about Julia, my half-sister—your niece, ma'am! Her continued residence with Lady Staveley has, for various reasons, proved impossible, and she has now returned to Canons Grange, our country estate at Woodham in Essex. She's a high-spirited young lady, but has, unfortunately, suffered some neglect in her education, and does not enjoy being alone, as she is unused to occupying herself profitably. In short, ma'am . . . I'm anxious to find a sensible companion of about her own age to be with her during my unfortunately frequent absences.'

Mr Hartwell broke off at this point, and looked in a deliberate and considering fashion at Caroline, who was caught in the act of studying his face with some interest. She had just made the unfortunately hasty decision that he was undoubtedly an arrogant man, completely wrapped up in his own interests, who clearly considered the female sex to be trivial and inferior, and would have no sympathy for a lonely young girl shut away in some gloomy mansion in the country, with no one to talk to, and probably not even a neighbour within reasonable distance for social intercourse. She lowered her eyes in some confusion, for the direct gaze of his dark eyes surprised her, as she had thought him oblivious of her presence, and gave her a nervous feeling that he knew what she was thinking.

'I hardly think you will find a suitable companion for Miss Hartwell in Stepney,' Mrs Barnes said uncooperatively. 'The neighbourhood is going down, and most of the better families are moving away; as, no doubt, we shall be doing ourselves before long.'

'Surely one of your daughters would welcome a

chance to move in a different society?' It was quite clear to Caroline's sensitive (and prejudiced) ear that he had only just managed to substitute 'different' for 'superior'.

'I do not suppose that Miss Hartwell's parents would consider a merchant's daughter fit company for their child,' Mrs Barnes said coldly.

'It was my father's suggestion,' Mr Hartwell countered.

'But you said that your father is in France!' Mrs Barnes was surprised enough to exclaim with a lively interest which contradicted her earlier apparent indifference.

'There are ways of communicating, at a price,' Mr Hartwell replied sardonically.

'Nevertheless, it has in the past been made clear to me that any connection between the Hartwell family and Trade would not be to their liking.' There was a distinctly bitter tinge in Mrs Barnes's voice, and Caroline looked at her sudden comprehension. So that was it! Lady Hartwell had married above her station, and had considered that Mrs Barnes had married below hers, and so had put her Beyond the Pale!

'As a matter of fact,' Mr Hartwell remarked, apparently to the mirror on the far side of the room, 'my paternal great-grandfather, who acquired the Barony by means of some rather shady dealings over the accession of King George I, was the grandson, on his mother's side, of a linen-draper.' He obviously assumed that this was sufficient to brush aside the long years of resentment which had simmered in Mrs Barnes's bosom, for he continued, 'Julia is seventeen, ma'am. I believe both your daughters to be a little older than that?'

'Miss Barnes is twenty, and Miss Alice Barnes eighteen,' Mrs Barnes replied absent-mindedly. She appeared to be preoccupied with some private thoughts.

'Alice has no more sense than a drunken hen, but Caroline might have a steadying effect on your sister —she has a reasonable intelligence and a studious disposition.' Having presumably reached some conclusion in her inner consideration, she fixed Mr Hartwell with a steely gaze, and demanded abruptly, 'What's the girl done? Got herself on the increase?'

'Certainly not!' Mr Hartwell was not in the least disconcerted by this sudden attack. 'Flighty she may be, but not entirely stupid! No, the problem is merely one of a lack of interest and a want of proper guidance.'

'And you think a girl of twenty will succeed where a grown woman has failed?'

'I think that the company of a sensible female of near her own age would be advantageous.'

There was silence for a few moments. Mrs Barnes gazed reflectively at her new Indian carpet, Mr Hartwell, frowning a little, waited expectantly, and Caroline, looking anxiously from one to the other, twisted her hands together and made up her mind to speak, having determined that she had no wish to oblige Mr Hartwell, or put herself in the way of his further acquaintance.

'How long would you wish me to stay?' she heard herself enquire in a calm voice, and was amazed, for this was not in the least what she had intended to say.

'It depends,' Mr Hartwell replied, turning his gaze full upon her again. 'I would suggest that a month's trial on both sides would give everyone concerned a chance to see how matters progress. If, after that, you felt at all unhappy about the arrangement, you would be under no obligation, and I should seek elsewhere. If, on the other hand, you and your cousin accord well together, I should be glad if you would stay as long as you please.'

'Are you proposing to employ my daughter?' Mrs Barnes enquired in an ominously icy tone.

'Miss Barnes would be our guest.' Mr Hartwell raised an eyebrow to register displeasure at being accused of such a solecism. 'She is, after all, a member of the family!'

'And was your ancestor a Freeman of the City of London?' Mrs Barnes enquired with apparent inconsequence.

'Good Heavens, no! A mere shopkeeper in Chelmsford!' Mr Hartwell replied with a suspicion of a smile. 'Does that make us too inferior to be recognised as relatives? I understand that Mr Barnes is a Freeman of the Mercers' Company, and an Alderman to boot!' His tone implied that he did not consider himself inferior to anyone, and Caroline suspected that he would have thought little of requiring the loan of a daughter from Queen Charlotte herself, had it suited his purposes.

Mrs Barnes gave a stately inclination of the head in acceptance of this proper recognition of relative rank, and said, 'I have no objection if Caroline chooses to accept your . . .' she paused judicially, '. . . your kind invitation.'

There was another short pause, during which Caroline lost her chance to voice an objection to the plan, for, unaccountably, she said nothing, and then Mr Hartwell said politely, 'Thank you, ma'am. Do you anticipate that Mr Barnes will have any objections?'

'Mr Barnes?' That gentleman's wife sounded mildly astounded that his name had even been mentioned. 'What has he to do with it? I have given my consent, and now the matter rests with Caroline.' And, with that, she apparently withdrew into a silent consideration of the brocade curtains which framed the window.

Mr Hartwell turned confidently to Caroline, and enquired, 'How say you, lady?' in the tones of one expecting an affirmative reply.

'What, precisely, would you wish me to do?' she asked.

He gave a little shrug which, to Caroline, appeared impatient. 'Whatever it is that young ladies do to pass their time in the country. Presumably there are occupations of interest and profit, but Julia seems to have no idea of them. She moons about all day, yawning and sulking, and will hardly stir out of doors. Whatever is suggested to her, she dismisses as boring.'

'Has she no friends or acquaintances at . . . where was it you said?' Caroline asked, puzzled that any reasonably intelligent female of seventeen should behave as he had described.

'Woodham. It's a small town, set between the River Lea and the Forest, and hardly above sixteen miles from here, so, if you've a mind at any time to visit your home, there would be no difficulty,' he replied, obviously seizing the opportunity to make the place sound more attractive to her. 'She's not lived at Canons Grange these past ten years to make any friends in the locality, and now has no wish to do so, as she finds fault with all she hears about our neighbours.'

'What does she say of the suggestion that I should be her companion?' Caroline asked, looking him very directly in the face. She was not surprised that his cool gaze slid aside for a moment, betraying the fact that the question had disconcerted him, but his recovery was immediate, and he shrugged, quirked his eyebrows, and said, 'I've no idea', in an indifferent tone, as if he did not much care, either.

Caroline felt sorry for Miss Hartwell, and decided that the poor girl must be much in need of an ally. She was probably too shy to make the first move to seek new friends, and undoubtedly this high-handed, arrogant brother must intimidate her.

'When would you wish me to come to Woodham?'

'As soon as may be convenient. I have, unfortunately, to go away for a few days next Monday, and it would be a great relief to me if you could be there to keep her company. I don't wish to leave her alone with only the servants in the house. I have to visit the City on business this Friday, and will call for you and your maid on my way home, if that would be acceptable.'

It seemed obvious to Caroline that he assumed that poor Miss Hartwell would do something idiotic if there was no one to keep an eye on her, and then she realised that he was also assuming that she had accepted his invitation, for he was waiting expectantly for her to say 'Yes,' and there had been no discernible hint of question in his last sentence. She recollected that she disliked what she knew about the country, that she had never been away from home alone before, that Miss Hartwell sounded a troublesome young lady, and that she had taken a misliking to Mr Hartwell, and had no wish to oblige him.

'Oh dear!' she exclaimed, 'but I share a maid with my sister!'

'Then I shall provide you with one from my own household,' he countered smoothly. 'I wouldn't wish to deprive Miss Alice Barnes of a valued attendant.'

Caroline looked hopefully at her mother, thinking that she might withdraw her permission over this problem, but she was looking at Mr Hartwell as she rose to her feet and said, 'That is settled, then, and we need detain you no longer, for I'm sure you have many more important matters to attend to. Miss Barnes will be ready on Friday at three of the clock in the afternoon, and you will, of course, bring the maid with you.'

Having made it clear that she had more important things to do this morning than settle to conversation with an unexpected visitor, that she intended to inspect the maid Mr Hartwell would provide, and that she expected her daughter to be properly chaperoned on her journey into the country, Miss Barnes rang the bell for James, gave the gentleman the tips of her fingers, and bade him a brisk 'Good morning'. Mr Hartwell found himself out of the house and entering his carriage in a remarkably short space of time, but Caroline noticed that he some-how managed to appear unhurried, and maintained an unfailing courtesy to the end. She observed from the window that he even turned at the door of his carriage to make an elegant little bow in her direction, although she would not have thought that she was visible to him, standing concealed by a curtain. She was summoned sharply by her mother to return to the wash-house before the carriage had drawn away from the door. Mrs Barnes resumed her normal placid direction of her monthly wash-day without a word about Mr Hartwell's visit, the recollection of which seemed to have escaped her memory.

Caroline, on the other hand, thought about it a great deal. Mr Hartwell, she decided, viciously shaking out a bolster-case, was undoubtedly a cold, domineering, heartless man, wholly lacking in sensibility. He probably hated his half-sister because she was the child of the second wife who had replaced his own mother. Poor Miss Hartwell—she must be exceedingly lonely and wretched, shut up in a desolate, echoing mansion in the depths of the country with nothing to do, and probably frightened half to death as well, for Canons Grange had an eerie ring to its name, like somewhere in a Gothic romance!

On the other hand, however sorry she might feel for the poor girl, Caroline had no wish to leave the bosom of her lively family and spend an indefinite time in the country, which she did not think she would enjoy, having viewed it only from a carriage window on occasional summer evening drives, from which she had received the impression that it was untidy, populated by unpleasant insects and fierce-looking animals (mostly with horns), and muddy.

There was no opportunity to discuss Mr Hartwell's invitation with her mother, for, by the time the washing was done, her father was due home from his counting-house, and he expected his dinner to be almost ready and his family dressed ready for it when he entered the house.

George, the eldest son of the family, was in India, and it happened that the Captain of a returning East India-man had that morning brought Mr Barnes news of him. In fact, it amounted to little more than the bare facts that he was well, and had recently been moved from Bombay to Calcutta, but the discussion of these titbits occupied the fond parents during the veal soup and the fried beefsteaks and potatoes, and it was not until the covers had been removed from the partridges and the jugged hare that Mrs Barnes's chance came to introduce a new topic of conversation.

'My sister's stepson honoured us with a visit this morning,' she announced in a wry tone.

'Sister?' Alice spoke uninvited. 'I didn't know you had a sister, Mama.'

'There appears to be a great deal which you do not know,' her father said quellingly, 'including when to hold your tongue, miss!'

Alice subsided, not wishing to be banished upstairs before the apple dumplings, and Mrs Barnes continued, 'He has invited Caroline to stay at Canons Grange with his half-sister for a few weeks.'

'Indeed?' Mr Barnes was sufficiently surprised to stop eating and to stare at his wife with his fork half-way to his mouth with a delectable morsel of partridge. 'And what has Lady Hartwell to say to that?'

'Nothing,' Mrs Barnes permitted herself a small smile. 'She's in France, a prisoner of Bonaparte!'

It would have been sheer cruelty to have refused to give any more information after arousing everyone's interest, and Mrs Barnes was not an unkind female. During the remainder of the course, she placidly informed her children that she was herself the younger of two sisters, the children of a country gentleman of no great wealth or title. Her sister had been married first, to the widowed Lord Hartwell, a Baron and a wealthy landowner, and the new Baroness had been mortified and angry when her sister had chosen to marry, as she considered, below her own natal station, let alone her new eminence, and to connect her with Trade!

'She cut me off at once!' Mrs Barnes told them. 'I was not particularly distressed,' she added, for her children had registered degrees of shocked protest, 'nor surprised, for Eleanor was always an almighty snob, and far higher in the instep than might pass for reasonable. It seems that Lord Hartwell suggested that Caroline might be invited, which shows that he, at least, has some sense.'

'And is she to go?' asked Mr Barnes, smiling at his wife's forbearance.

Caroline opened her mouth to say 'No!', but was forestalled by her mother's assured, 'Of course! It will do her a world of good to spend a little time in the fresh country air, for she's looked a mite peaky of late, and who knows what may come of it?' She directed a meaning look at her husband, who nodded thoughtfully and carved himself a morsel or two more of the roast partridge.

'I'm not sure . . .' Caroline ventured, frowning a little.

Mr Barnes turned a benign and tolerant gaze upon her, and said kindly, 'You've nothing to fear, you know. If anyone attempts to give you a set-down, just remember that you are the daughter of a Freeman of the City of London, who is as good as any man in England! When are you to go?'

'Mr Hartwell will call for her himself on Friday.' Mrs Barnes answered for her daughter, who was still frowning. 'There is the matter of clothes, of course.'

'I have plenty of clothes . . .' Caroline began, not wishing to put her father to any expense for the benefit of Mr Hartwell, but she was over-ruled.

'The new blue silk will do well enough for ordinary evening wear, but your muslins are all washed limp after the hot summer, and you'll need some sturdy boots for country walking.' Mrs Barnes, who had obviously been thinking the matter over while she presided over her wash-day, reeled off what seemed a very long list of necessary articles of clothing which it was suitable to mention in mixed company, and there would appear likely to be another list of unmentionables to follow in private. Caroline thought that Mr Hartwell would need to hire a wagon to carry her luggage, but kept the thought to herself and ate her apple dumpling in silence, letting her mother's monologue flow over her almost unheard while she considered the unpleasing prospect of a month in the country, and hoped that Mr Hartwell would be away himself for most of it on one of his 'frequent absences', and she wondered vaguely where he went that required visiting so often.

The evening seemed unending to Caroline, who felt herself every minute to be more deeply committed to a course which she had no desire to follow, but she realised that the moment for saying that she would not go had passed long before, had slipped through her grasp when she had failed to answer Mr Hartwell's 'How say you, lady?' with a direct refusal.

'Oh, Caro! How lucky you are!' Alice exclaimed the moment after the closing of the door to their bedroom. 'I thought we'd never come to bed tonight, and I've been bursting to ask you all about him!'

'Ladies do not burst!' Caroline said repressively. 'And, pray, who is "him"—he,' she corrected herself swiftly.

'How lucky you are,' Alice sighed again. 'A whole month in the country, at least, with new people to meet, and a very handsome gentleman to squire you about. Just think, Caro! You may make a very good marriage, if you make the most of your chances!'

'If you have Mr Hartwell in mind as the other partner to it, you may cease to speculate!' Caroline replied tartly. 'I don't think him particularly handsome, but I do find him quite disagreeable!'

'Disagreeable?' Alice exclaimed. 'Oh, Caro! How can you? A good-looking, well-set-up young gentleman' (Alice had not actually set eyes upon Mr Hartwell, but one would not have thought so to hear her enthusiasm!) 'with goodness knows how many thousand a year, and estates all over the place! How can he possibly be disagreeable?'

'He seems to find it quite easy,' Caroline replied with some amusement at her sister's method of judging whether or no a man might be agreeable. 'Besides, we know of only one estate, and that's not his, but his father's. He seems to me a very high-handed, arrogant sort of person, and I'm sure I shall not like him in the least!'

'Then why are you going to stay with him?'

'For his sister's sake. The poor girl must be quite wretched, shut away in the country with nothing to do, no friends, no companion, and a thoroughly tyrannical brother to order her goings and comings. Why, the only half-way kind thing he said about her was to admit her to be not entirely stupid. Poor Julia! I shall love her like a sister, I feel sure, and contrive some way to make Mr Hartwell treat her more considerately.'

On that resolution, she put out the candles and composed herself to sleep, feeling almost reconciled to the prospect of a whole wearisome month amid the mud, the insects and the horned beasts.

The prospect of a new wardrobe was not without its attraction, even to a young lady of reasonable intelligence and a studious disposition, and there was hardly time to think of anything else during the rest of the week, for Mrs Barnes had a great liking for fabrics and trimmings, which her thrifty nature seldom allowed her to indulge, and she found a great if vicarious pleasure in seeing that her elder daughter should go out into the great world with a suitable equipment of muslins, silks, merinoes, velvets and cambrics, all with the latest in braids and laces, bows and buttons. New bonnets were viewed and selected, gloves and hose purchased by the dozen, and the suitable walking-boots found and brought home for one of the housemaids to wear continuously for two days, that they might be properly broken in.

Mr Barnes played his small part in all this in a princely fashion, for he not only provided the guineas for his wife's purchases, but made a personal contribution of a pearl necklace and the freedom of his warehouse, from which Caroline was allowed to choose and carry off three of his best cashmere shawls.

Friday arrived all too soon. By ten minutes before three on the fateful afternoon, the trunk stood in the hall, with half a dozen bandboxes piled about it, and Caroline, in a smart crimson redingote trimmed hussar-fashion with black braid, and a black bonnet trimmed with crimson feathers, had bidden farewell to the servants, their ginger cat and her family, and was sitting nervously in the parlour, awaiting the arrival of Mr Hartwell.

CHAPTER
TWO

THE CHIMES of the clock in St Dunstan's tower were not melodious, and to Caroline they sounded like the Knell of Doom, particularly as they were accompanied by the clopping of hoofs and the grinding of wheels as Mr Hartwell's chaise arrived at the door, drawn by four fine matched chestnuts and complete with postilions and outriders. What was more, it was followed by a second vehicle, intended, it transpired, solely for the transporting of Miss Barnes's baggage.

The maid was brought in for Mrs Barnes's inspection and approbation, which was given readily as she proved to be a well-spoken woman of thirty or so, with a pleasant apple-cheeked face and a very neat, clean appearance. Even her name, Martha, had a most respectable ring to it, and Mrs Barnes knew instinctively that here was a female who might safely be entrusted with the care of Caroline's wardrobe, the laundering of her linen and the proper maintenance of ostrich plumes and fine French lace. Caroline herself, of course, was not considered to have anything to say to the matter, but she had taken a liking to the woman, so this hardly mattered.

A chaise was a comfortable vehicle for two, but was usually a trifle crowded with a third passenger, but, with what Caroline chose to consider typical perversity on his part, Mr Hartwell had contrived to own a chaise which was broader and longer in the body than usual, and there was ample room for Martha to sit between Caroline and her host, providing the sop to propriety which Mrs Barnes desired. This, however, did make conversation somewhat difficult, as Martha, although not, of course, saying anything herself, formed a barrier which Mr Hartwell was forced to speak over, round or through whenever he wished to address an observation or question to Caroline, and her rather brief replies seemed to become muffled to near-inaudibility on their way round, over or through back to him.

Nevertheless, Caroline was informed in due course that the first manufactory of porcelain in England once stood near to Bow Bridge, that Stratford was mentioned in Chaucer's *Canterbury Tales*, that Leyton, a charming village, was fast becoming built up and would soon join on to London, and various other titbits of information and opinion which might enliven the journey and make the passing scene more interesting for her.

'Pray, what are those animals in that field?' Caroline enquired not long after they had passed Chingford church. This was the first exchange which she had initiated, but her puzzlement over the beasts required enlightenment.

'Sheep,' Mr Hartwell replied succinctly, sounding, even in that one word, detestably superior and amused by her ignorance.

'But they have horns!' Caroline protested. 'Are they all rams?'

'No. I believe they're a Dorset breed—some varieties have horned females, you know.'

Caroline was silent, for she had seen few sheep in the flesh (except roast or boiled) and drew what knowledge she had of them from an instructive book about domestic animals which she had been given as a child. She decided to ask no more questions, as she had no wish to appear ignorant to the insufferable Mr Hartwell, but her resolve was broken within minutes.

The road had been meandering along on the edge of rising ground above the broad plain of the narrow river, which was occasionally visible on their left. On their right, the land had been rising for some time, unnoticed by Caroline who was seated on the near-side of the chaise, but she happened to glance across to the other side, and saw that the skyline was now filled by a great dark mass, which advanced in places within half a mile of the road.

Startled, she leaned forward to see better, and exclaimed, 'Why, what a great number of trees!'

'The Forest,' Mr Hartwell said as if introducing it to her. 'It formerly covered most of Essex, but we have now but the remains of it, running all along the ridge there as far as just beyond Horsing, with a few patches more to the north. You'll find some picturesque scenes in it for your sketch-book—you do draw, do you not?'

The question might have been asked out of interest, but to Caroline it sounded more like an implied slur on the assumed lack of accomplishments to be expected in a daughter of Trade.

'Indeed,' she replied coolly, 'when I have time'— which was true. No need, she thought, to add that she had not found time for about a year. 'Does Cousin Julia draw well?'

'No,' replied Mr Hartwell judiciously. 'I would not say she does anything well. In fact, when she chooses to do anything at all, which is not often, she manages in general to do it badly.'

Caroline felt Martha make a little movement, not unlike a wriggle, which was accompanied by a small sniff, and she wondered what it implied.

A couple of miles further on, Mr Hartwell remarked that he wished to call at a house along their way for a few minutes, if Caroline would indulge him, and presently the chaise drew up at the roadside before a plain yellowish brick cottage on the right-hand side, and he got down and disappeared round the back of it in the matter of one on easy terms of calling with whoever resided there.

The other vehicle with the luggage passed and went on, the postilions dismounted and stood about talking to the outriders, who also got down, and one of them made some adjustment to the harness. Caroline looked out of the window at the field across the road, which contained three large trees and half a dozen bored-looking brown cows. They had seen very little traffic for some time, and she looked with anticipation along the road in the direction which she was facing as she heard the sound of approaching hoofs, and presently a single horse and rider appeared.

She expected that the horseman would pass quite close, as the chaise was standing on the wrong side of the road, but he checked as he came nearer, and slowed almost to a halt, staring at the chaise, which had the arms of Lord Hartwell on the door, and side-stepped his black mount to the far side of the road.

He was a tall, broad-shouldered man on a big horse, Caroline saw, dressed in a broadcloth coat with a snowy cravat. His boots shone through a light film of dust, and his hat was a glossy beaver—obviously a gentleman. She made some slight inadvertent movement, and the man's gaze, which had been on the chaise, turned full on her. He started his horse forward, then checked again, looking at her with a slight frown, which faded into a charming smile as he raised his hat to her and bowed. She received a brief impression of fair, wavy hair, a handsome, strong-featured face and a pleasant expression, and then he replaced his hat, set his horse in motion, and rode past and on down the road.

Caroline craned her neck to look after him, wondering whom he might be, and felt a lightening of her spirits as it occurred to her that he might live in the vicinity and form one of the new circle of acquaintances to which she might hope to be introduced during her stay in Woodham.

'I'm sorry to have kept you waiting,' an unwanted voice cut across her thoughts as Mr Hartwell re-entered the chaise. 'I trust you have not found the waiting too tedious?'

Caroline gave him a faint smile and murmured something politely complaisant, then added, 'I was contemplating the countryside. I've not had much acquaintance with it in the past.' She felt that she must make some endeavour to be sociable for fear he might think her gauche or even—horrid thought!—ill bred.

'Ah, yes—the countryside.' Mr Hartwell leaned forward and surveyed it through the window on Caroline's side. 'Those, I believe, are oak trees, and the—er —animals are cows.'

'Yes,' said Caroline frostily, her good resolutions vanishing in a cloud of pique. 'I know.'

'On further consideration,' Mr Hartwell went on as if she had not spoken, in a maddeningly equable fashion, 'one of them is a hawthorn—the trees, I mean. The cows are all cows.'

'One of 'em's an 'effer,' Martha said in a small voice. 'If you please, sir,' she added hastily.

'Quite right.' Mr Hartwell remained unruffled, and Caroline was left wondering what an 'effer' might be, as the chaise gave a preliminary lurch and set off again up a long, steep hill. At the top, Mr Hartwell called to the postilions to stop, and requested Caroline to step down for a moment to look at the view before them.

It was not spectacular, but pleasantly and essentially English. The centre of the middle distance was occupied by a four-square white church tower of impressive size, crowned by a black cross and a golden weathercock, and below it could be seen the dark slate roof of a large church. Clustered about it were the red-tiled roofs of a small town, nestling amid a fine patchwork quilt of enclosed fields of various colours, and bordered on

Caroline's left by broad meadows threaded by two or three streams, on one of which a string of barges was moving slowly along.

Between the town and the river stood a cluster of dark, ominous-looking buildings, and to the north, on ground rising from the meadows, she could make out an array of wooden buildings in neat rows about an open space, in the centre of which a white flag-pole was flying a patch of bright colour, but it was too far away for her to determine whether or no it was a Union flag.

'Woodham,' Mr Hartwell said casually, waving a hand towards the town. 'The river, to your left, is here divided into several streams, two of which provide the motive power for several mills, the largest, which is that cluster of sinister-looking buildings, being a gunpowder manufactory. There is an army camp beyond the town. These two offspring of Bellona provide the main sources of income in the town, other than agriculture, of course. They've been a godsend, as the townspeople have felt the pinch of poverty since the Abbey was dissolved.'

'When was that?' Caroline asked, looking for some sign of such a building.

'In 1540.'

'Oh—of course! Henry VIII!' Caroline felt a little foolish, but his mention of the Dissolution had made it sound a more recent event. 'Where is—was—the Abbey? Is there nothing left of it?'

'In the middle of the town. The present parish church is all that remains of it.'

'Ah, yes—I thought it a large church for so small a town. And whereabouts is Canons Grange? Is it that fantastical edifice with the turrets?'

'No, that is Pinnacles, the residence of Viscount Cressing. He keeps sheep. Hornless.'

Caroline had already deduced the nature of the moving white dots, which seemed to occupy a large part of

the land between the town and the Forest, and was
relieved to hear that they were hornless. She made no
comment, however, and Mr Hartwell continued, extending a pointing hand, 'And Canons Grange is over
there. You'll not make it out easily, but follow the line of
my arm . . .'

He moved close to Caroline, put his other arm about
her shoulders and leaned his face close to hers, in order
to make a more direct line between her eyes and the
direction in which he was pointing. Caroline felt herself
give a little start, as if in surprise, and was puzzled that
this should have happened, especially as it was followed
by a very curious sensation which ran through her
body—like, she thought, very hot water. It took her a
few moments to collect herself, and then she realised
that Mr Hartwell's pointing finger was indicating the
grey roof which peeped out from the trees below the
ridge crowned by a Lombardy poplar.

'I see it!' she exclaimed. 'Below the poplar tree.'

'Yes. My grandfather planted that the year King
George came to the throne, so it will be sixty years old
next year. The house appears from here to be sur-
rounded by trees, but you'll find it has a fine, open
prospect, from the front, at least.'

'The house must be very old.'

'Parts of it are as much as six centuries old, but there
are later additions, some Tudor, some of the last century. You'll not be expected to sleep in a stone-floored
cell with no glass in the windows, or dine in a vast,
draughty Great Hall! We manage to be tolerably
comfortable.'

Caroline, who was as fond of a Gothic novel as any
right-mindedly romantic young female, was pleased to
hear that part of the house had an interesting history,
and might prove to be both picturesque and reminiscent
of ghastly happenings and horrible events, but her

practical nature drew encouragement from Mr Hartwell's 'tolerably comfortable' pronounced in what sounded to her like tones of smug satisfaction, and promised something more than merely tolerable.

'We even have a ghost, they say, but I've not seen him.' Mr Hartwell spoke calmly as if he referred only to an interesting piece of furniture. 'Apparently he is, or was, one of the Abbots—the last, presumably—who wanders about keeping an eye on things. Quite harmless.'

'Was he horribly done to death by King Henry like the poor Carthusians?' Caroline enquired hopefully. 'Is he unable to rest until his murder is avenged?'

'Oh, nothing of that sort!' Mr Hartwell replied with a slight frown. 'He retired on a very handsome pension, in fact. I can't imagine why he should bother to haunt the Grange—he probably never came near it in life. Shall we go on? It puts Cook in an ill-humour if dinner is late, and that's more to be feared than the ghost of a long-dead Abbot!'

The road proceeded downhill in a leisurely fashion, and then passed the town instead of going through it, as Caroline had expected. Mr Hartwell called to the postilions to slow down as they passed the end of the town, and Caroline caught a glimpse of a narrow street lined with a mixture of brick- and plaster-fronted shops of uneven heights and widths.

The road was remarkably crooked, and she mused on crooked stiles and sixpences until they reached a particularly sharp bend, where a neat little lodge-house, looking rather like a thatched tea-caddy, sat above the road beside a handsome pair of wrought-iron gates. The chaise turned off and passed through the gateway, with a proper accompaniment of bows and curtsies from the lodge-keeper and his wife, and then climbed up a drive which wound quite steeply amid some very handsome

specimen trees, and finally emerged on a broad
gravelled terrace before a large, rambling house of
extremely irregular appearance.

Caroline had no time for more than one startled look
at the strange mixture of stone, brick, timber and plaster
and the variety of window shapes and roof lines before
she passed through a splendid Tudor doorway into the
house. She would have liked to take a longer look, but it
seemed ill mannered to linger outside when her host was
obviously in something of a hurry to go within-doors,
as if he had some unpleasant duty ahead which he
preferred to have done with as quickly as possible.

The entrance hall was square and imposing, but dark
with oak panelling and heavy beams, with only a few dim
portraits, a single vase of flowers and a full-sized marble
copy of the Apollo Belvedere to lighten the gloom. Mr
Hartwell tossed his beaver hat on to the outstretched
hand of Apollo with an accuracy born of long practice,
greeted the butler who appeared to welcome them with a
brisk, 'All well, Carter?', and ushered Caroline across
the hall and through a door into the room on the right of
the front entrance, without giving her time even to
remove her redingote.

The sun, which was now declining in a blaze of golden
splendour, illuminated the room through two large oriel
windows, and Caroline's first impression was of warmth
and light, for the furniture was modern, made of satin-
wood and upholstered in bright chintzes, the walls were
a pleasant pale ochre, the fireplace, which was enormous, made of honey-coloured marble carved elaborately with a great achievement of arms and a variety of
small heraldic beasts, the floor covered with a light-
coloured floral carpet, and the ceiling painted to match
it, like a mirror-image.

The only occupants of the room were a young lady and
a small white dog of indeterminate breed and shaggy

appearance, which sprang to its feet and launched itself
at Mr Hartwell's legs, as if it intended to savage his
boots. The young lady looked up in a languid fashion
from the book which she was obviously not reading,
sighed, and rose slowly from the sofa on which she had
been lounging, and remarked in a bored tone, 'Oh,
you're back. Is this my gaoler?'

'Down, Horatio!' Mr Hartwell exclaimed, at which
the dog sat down and looked up at him in a puzzled
fashion for a moment, then dubiously wagged its tail as if
not altogether convinced that this was Master and not a
house-breaker. 'Your cousin Julia,' Mr Hartwell said to
Caroline, 'who may or may not summon up sufficient
grace to greet you properly.'

'Good afternoon, Miss Barnes,' Julia Hartwell said
distantly, looking past Caroline's left ear. 'I trust you
had a pleasant journey and are not overly fatigued. My
brother's unmitigated company can be very wearisome.'

Caroline regarded her cousin thoughtfully, wondering
how best to reply. She was a remarkably pretty girl, with
dark curly hair cut short, just the style which Caroline
would have chosen for herself, and a graceful figure
marred by a tendency to droop. For a moment, Caroline
thought that she must have seen her before at some time,
and then she realised that her familiar appearance was
due to a strong resemblance to herself.

'Why, I do believe we might pass for sisters!' she
exclaimed, smiling. 'Yes, thank you, Cousin Julia—I
had a very pleasant journey, much enlivened by your
brother's instructive conversation.'

Julia looked directly at her for the first time, her dark
eyes wide and a little wary, and then remarked in a sour
tone, 'I suppose the instruction was mostly how you are
to spy on me and worm your way into my confidence so
that you may report all my doings and plans to him.'

'In fact,' Caroline replied smoothly, sitting down

gracefully, if uninvited, on the nearest chair, 'it was, in the main, concerned with sheep and cows and history. I don't recall any mention of worms, or of you, for that matter. I understood that you were in need of a little companionship in your lonely exile in the country, but if you don't wish me to be here, I shall be quite happy to return home in the morning. I do not stay where I am unwelcome.'

She spoke gently and pleasantly, but with a degree of firmness which suprised her even more than her hearers. Mr Hartwell, still standing near the door with the dog, regarded her with thoughtful interest, raised his eyebrows a trifle, and rubbed a hand over his mouth and chin as if he were either wondering whether he needed to shave, or hiding a smile.

'Oh!' said Julia, disconcerted. 'I—I'm sorry, Cousin Caroline!' She hesitated, looking young, unhappy and confused. 'Yes, I am very much alone here, and I should be glad of your company. I—I thought you would be—well, older, and—and pernickety! Robert said you would teach me how to behave, so I thought . . .' Her voice tailed off, and she drooped even more.

'I think,' said Mr Hartwell, 'that it might be as well to start afresh. We shall assume that we have just entered the room—no, Horatio! You need not investigate me again.' The dog looked fixedly at Mr Hartwell's boots, then retired to his former place before the hearth, which was filled with a fine display of flowers, and grumbled to himself at intervals. His master continued, 'Pray, let me make you known to one another—Cousin Caroline, your cousin Julia—Julia, your cousin Caroline.'

Caroline, a little disconcerted that she had suddenly become 'Cousin' to Mr Hartwell too, stood up and advanced on Julia, took her firmly by the shoulders and kissed her cheek, murmuring a polite, 'So happy to make your acquaintance.' Julia stiffened momentarily, then returned the kiss and murmured equally politely, 'Welcome to Canons Grange, dear Cousin,' and then dissolved into laughter, at which Caroline, in relief at the sudden easing of tension, joined in.

'Oh, dear!' Julia exclaimed at last, wiping her eyes on a minute handkerchief, 'I had quite made up my mind that you'd be horrid and old-maidish, and now I find you're really quite a pleasant person after all!'

'I told you!' Mr Hartwell murmured, raising his eyes to heaven in exasperation. 'Females! Did you think to order tea, Julia?'

Before his sister could admit that she had not, the tea equipage arrived of its own accord, assisted by two footmen, and a little highly artificial conversation followed, largely for the benefit of the servants, who must never be allowed to suspect that there was any dissension in the Family. Julia displayed the good manners which her brother had said she did not possess, and showed great interest in the details of the names, ages, occupations and whereabouts of Caroline's sister and brothers, although she did pout a little and express disappointment that George was a clerk in the Company, and not a soldier.

'A red coat so becomes a man!' she declared. 'I do wish Robert would purchase a pair of colours . . .'

'. . . and get himself killed in Portugal, along with all the other poor fellows!' Mr Hartwell finished for her in a sardonic tone.

'Oh, not at all! Anyway, there's no fighting in Portugal,' Julia protested.

'Don't be too sure of that!' her brother replied darkly. 'We've sent an army there, you know—or do you? Why do you never read a news-sheet, Julia?'

'Because the ink comes off and makes my hands dirty,' Julia replied. 'In any case, I'd have thought you'd wish to serve your country. You tell me that I should do things because it's my duty—don't you have any duties?'

'Yes, a great many, and some of them *are* of service to our country.'

'Oh, and what, pray? Travelling about and farming?'

'Indeed. Since the Americans refuse to trade with any of the combatants, we must produce enough food to keep ourselves, or starve. Do you not realise, Julia, that, due to the shortage of corn, its price has risen by fifty per cent in the past year?'

'What exactly is fifty per cent?' Julia enquired airily, as if the matter was of no great importance.

'Your brother means that a quarter of corn cost sixty-six shillings last year, but ninety-nine shillings this year,' Caroline said quietly. 'For a labouring family, that means that they must pay almost as much for six loaves this year as they did for ten last year.'

'Oh,' said Julia blankly, and put down the dainty little cake she had just taken from a plateful offered by one of the footmen. 'Well, I shall not say "Let them eat cake" like a certain other empty-pated ninny-hammer we have all heard about! Henry' (this to the footman with the cakes, who was standing looking suitably wooden-faced), 'Henry, do your family have enough to eat?'

Henry glanced sideways at his colleague for support, but he was gazing stolidly into space, deaf, apparently, as a post, so Henry was forced to summon up his courage and answer, a trifle hoarsely, 'Yes, thank'ee, ma'am.'

'Really?' Julia pressed him.

'Well, you see, ma'am—we're lucky, because of the scraps.'

'Scraps?'

'Bits and ends left over, ma'am. Mr Carter—'e's the butler, ma'am' (in case she was unaware of Carter's identity), ''e lets us take 'em 'ome—home—when we goes.'

Caroline could not resist looking at Mr Hartwell, to

see his reaction to the news that his butler gave away food from his kitchen, but he appeared unmoved by the revelation, and, happening to glance at Caroline and catch her eye, gave her a considering look and quirked one eyebrow.

'Oh, good,' said Julia. 'I'm glad to hear it. Well, if anyone is having particular difficulty at home, they must let us know. I'm aware that some of you come from quite—er—large families.'

Caroline thought she had been about to say 'poor' rather than 'large' and nodded to herself in approval at the tactful change. It seemed that Julia, although a little ignorant and thoughtless in some respects, was sound at heart.

With the serving of tea completed, the footmen withdrew, Henry still a little red about the ears over having Opened His Mouth in the Drawing-Room. As soon as the door closed behind them, Julia said, 'I suppose you'll put a stop to that now, Robert? Well, if you do, I shall think you even more horrid than I already do!'

'Oh dear!' Mr Hartwell replied with a irritating calmness. 'I really cannot imagine how I may continue to bear the burden of your dislike.'

'If you are too skinflint to spare a few scraps and left-overs to poor people who may be very hungry, I think you quite beyond everything!' Julia flared at him. 'And I'm sure you'll be punished for it!'

Mr Hartwell sighed and rose to his feet. 'Well, before I suffer the fate of Dives, I shall go and change for dinner,' he said. 'I suggest that you show Cousin Caroline to her room so that she may do the same, or she'll be put to a rush.'

'Dives? Pray, what has he to do with it?' Julia demanded, as he moved in an unhurried fashion towards the door.

'St Luke. Chapter sixteen, I believe,' Mr Hartwell

replied. 'And before you condemn me, try to recall who gives Carter his orders. Excuse me, Cousin Caroline, Julia.' He went out.

'Dives,' Julia said thoughtfully, and looked questioningly at Caroline.

'And Lazarus,' she prompted.

'Oh, yes. I remember. And, of course, Robert gives Carter his orders, so I suppose that means that I should mind my business and not interfere in the running of the household! Oh, Cousin Caro! We're not a very happy family, are we? I do wish Mama and Papa would come home, and then everything would be right again. I do miss them!' Julia drooped despondently, the corners of her mouth turning down in a most woebegone fashion. 'Oh, well,' she sighed, 'you'd best come and see your room, or we'll be late for dinner, and that will be my fault again!'

To Caroline, who was used to a much smaller house, the walk to her room seemed very long, but not particularly complicated. Julia led her across the gloomy hall, up a fine, wide oak staircase and along a gallery hung with tapestries, but the light was too dim and the tapestries too old and faded to make out what they depicted. Two or three suits of armour were disposed between the closed oak-panelled doors which appeared on either side at intervals, and Julia gave some slight indication of what was behind some of them by saying 'Mama's room. Mary's room—that's my sister, you know, who is with poor dear Mama in France. My room. This is Robert's, at the corner—Papa's is the other way,' gesturing behind them. 'And round the corner, here is yours. I do hope you'll like it.'

She flung open the door on a very handsome room, lit by the declining sun, with walls panelled in light-coloured wood, and very elegant furniture in the style of Mr Hepplewhite, which, although now considered by some to be a little out of date, was exactly what Caroline would like to have chosen for herself. All the pieces were neatly inlaid with a pattern of wreathed flowers in various fruit-woods, and the toilet china on the wash-stand and dressing-table was painted with similar wreaths in colour. It was not until the next day that Caroline realised that the same wreaths were woven into the pattern of the cream-grounded carpet, curtains and bed-hangings.

'I would like to have given you a grander room,' Julia said doubtfully, 'but Robert said this one would do very well, and you might like the outlook.'

Caroline went to the window to inspect the view. There were two windows, side by side, with a long mirror between them, and each had a wide window-seat, plentifully supplied with cushions. They looked out on a wide prospect, diagonally to the south-west across the valley, with the sturdy shape of the church tower of Woodham squarely in the middle, the red roofs clustered about it, and the weathercock catching the rays of the setting sun. Below the terrace at the front of the house, the grounds sloped down the long hill towards the road, but that was invisible behind trees and shrubbery, and the garden seemed to descend in stages, with meandering paths and little flights of steps, in an artfully informal fashion. Beyond where she judged the road to be, there were fields, some ploughed, some filled with growing things of various colours, mostly shades of green, and some dotted about with beasts. The sun glittered brightly on distant water, but its disc was already touching a tree-covered ridge, miles away across the valley, where a single church spire stood against a clear sky.

'It's a very fine view,' Caroline admitted, feeling surprised that Mr Hartwell should have the sensibility to realise that she would enjoy it, and wondering if she still had enough skill with pencil and brush to make a sketch of it.

'Yes, but please don't linger over it now!' Julia said nervously. 'Robert does hate to be kept waiting for his dinner. See, Martha is here to help you, and I'll come back for you in half an hour.'

Caroline turned away from the window to make some reply, but found that Julia had disappeared, presumably to her own room, and it was Martha who stood in the doorway, the newly-pressed blue silk evening gown held up for her approval.

CHAPTER
THREE

THE EVENING proved to be very trying. To begin with, it was well past the promised half-hour before Julia reappeared, and Caroline had dismissed Martha and ventured out into the passage twice to listen for some sign of life, but heard nothing. Eventually, she decided to make her own way downstairs, and had just reached the corner into the main corridor when Julia came full tilt round it and almost knocked her over.

She was full of breathless apologies, and some complicated tale of an accident to her gown, but Caroline was unable to make much sense of it as the girl had seized her arm and was hurrying her downstairs with unseemly haste even as she spoke.

They returned to the room that Caroline had first entered, and which she now gathered from Julia's breathless talk was known as the parlour, and, as they came in, Mr Hartwell, who had been standing at the window apparently surveying the sunset, drew his watch from his pocket, looked at it in a pointed fashion, then crossed to the fireplace without a word and tugged at the bell-pull which hung beside it.

Carter entered, bowed slightly, and made a formal declaration that dinner was served. His master silently offered Caroline his arm, and conducted her across the hall to an oak-panelled dining-room full of heavy, old-fashioned furniture. Julia followed behind with a murmured, 'I'm sorry, Robert—it was my fault', to which her brother replied with only a vague 'Mm', which sounded to Caroline as if it signified that it was no more than he expected.

The meal was served in a very formal fashion, which Caroline found unnerving, for she was used to a far more casual way of life at home, where conversation, although dominated by her parents, was free-flowing, as the whole family sat closely together about a round table, and the servants, having brought in each course, withdrew while it was eaten. At Canons Grange they appeared to dine *en famille* with all the ceremony of a formal dinner. The table was long enough to seat a dozen in comfort, but Mr Hartwell took his place at the head, Julia at the foot, and Caroline was midway between them on the side to Mr Hartwell's right, and felt that she was at such a distance from either that conversation had to be conducted across an ocean of white damask.

To make matters worse, the meal was served by three footmen, albeit in country livery, not the intimidating splendour of powdered wigs and silk stockings. Their constant presence put anything but the most general remarks out of the question, and Caroline felt that this was quite as uncomfortable as dining at the Mansion House.

'I trust that your room is to your liking?' Mr Hartwell enquired during the soup, which was fish of some sort —something which Caroline particularly disliked.

'Yes, thank you,' she replied briefly, recollecting that, according to Julia, he had not thought it necessary to allocate her anything better than a room which would 'do' (although even she had to admit that it was a very pleasant room). Not wishing to appear ungracious, she added, 'It has a fine view.'

'Yes.'

'It seems not very far to Woodham across the fields.'

'Not much above a mile. Perhaps you may persuade Julia to bestir herself to walk there with you.'

'The path is usually very muddy,' Julia observed, and

that appeared to finish that topic, although Mr Hartwell looked for a moment as if he might have said something disagreeable had the servants not been present.

The rest of the meal progressed in much the same way, with a variety of dishes, all rather elaborately cooked with sauces and garnishes to which Caroline was unused, and with wine, which she seldom had at home, for her father allowed it to the young people only on special occasions. It made her feel unpleasantly warm about the cheeks, and not quite in control of her words.

The second course was almost finished before anyone spoke again, and then Caroline, finding the silence oppressive, enquired of Mr Hartwell, 'Did you say that you have to go away on Monday?'

'Yes,' he replied, but did not seem inclined to enlarge on this. Caroline, however, had made up her mind to hold a conversation, so she plunged on, 'I suppose you must be kept very busy, managing your father's estates.'

'Not particularly,' he replied coolly. 'He has only one other, and that's let at present.'

'You'll not tempt my brother to talk of his travels,' Julia put in from her end of the table. 'I think he does something very wicked and disgraceful, for he never gives more than some vague idea of where he's going before he leaves, and says nothing about where he's been when he returns.' She spoke in an arch and provoking fashion, as if determined to annoy him.

Mr Hartwell nodded to one of the footmen to clear the plates and dishes, and said flatly, 'Where I go and what I do wouldn't interest you in the slightest. It's nothing but a tale of posthouses and sordid haggling. Do you go much into the City, Cousin Caroline?'

'Quite often.' Caroline was relieved that he seemed to have opened the door to a proper conversation at last. 'Some of my father's friends still live there, and we go to visit them, and to shop, of course.'

'How can anyone live in the City?' Julia asked in a wondering tone. 'Why, it's all counting-houses and warehouses, and the streets are so narrow and crowded! Everyone lives in the newer parts, surely, about Piccadilly and Grosvenor Square, and then only in the Season.'

'A great many people live in the City,' Caroline replied, smiling, 'and not only in the Season! My father's friends are merchants and bankers, and many still like to live near their places of business. I must admit, though, that more and more are moving out to the villages around London, as we have done.'

'Oh, Trade!' Julia said dismissively. 'How horrid for you to have to mix with tradespeople.'

'Not at all!' Caroline exclaimed indignantly, forgetting about the footmen. 'Why should I find it horrid to mix with people of my own sort? My family is Trade, but we're not ashamed of it. My father is a Freeman of the City of London, and as good as any man in the country!'

She spoke with some heat, lifting her chin proudly, then found that Mr Hartwell was regarding her with a smile which looked to her to be decidedly sarcastic, and his 'Bravo, Cousin Caroline! That puts you in your place, Miss Hartwell!' quite deflated her.

'I'm sorry,' she said. 'I should not have spoken so.'

'It is Julia who should apologise,' Mr Hartwell said quietly, looking at his sister, but she merely clamped her lips together mutinously and scowled, and the rest of dinner passed mainly in silence, broken only by the most formal of polite questions and answers, and those only at long intervals.

At last, the two ladies withdrew and left Mr Hartwell to his port and cigar. Julia led the way to the parlour, where the curtains had been drawn, candles brought in, and the flowers in the hearth replaced by a wood fire, before which Horatio lay in an abandoned attitude, snoring gently.

'I'm sorry,' Julia said in a subdued tone once they were inside the room and the door was shut. 'When I lived with my godmother, she was always saying things about Trade, and making fun of shop-keepers' wives who ape fashionable ladies, and so did all her friends. I suppose I just fell into that way of thinking and speaking, and—well—I forgot, for you're not at all as I imagined a merchant's daughter to be.'

'You mean I might almost pass as a lady?' Caroline asked wryly. 'Don't worry about it—I know how Society people regard us, and I don't overmuch care! How do you usually pass your evenings?'

'Oh, Robert never drinks but half a glass of port and smokes one cigar, and then he comes and sits in here for a while and reads me improving pieces from the news-sheet, or conducts conversation. We don't get on, as I suppose you've noticed.' And she pulled a little face, rolling her eyes in a droll manner.

'What did you do with your time when you lived with your godmother?' Caroline asked curiously, for she was not sure what pastimes were indulged in by Society ladies.

'Usually we dined out, or had people to dinner, and there were cards and dancing, and a great deal of talk—you know—all the usual things people do. That was when we were in Town or at Brighton or Bath. In the country, we had people to stay, or we went to stay with them, and there were Assembly Rooms in the two nearest towns, and a theatre in one. There were always so many people, so it was easy to find things to do; but here, with no one but ourselves . . . Oh, Cousin Caro! It's so dull, dull, *dull*! What would you be doing if you were at home?'

'We talk, and play games sometimes. Alice and I sew,

and my brothers read the news-sheets and tell us about what they've been doing during the day, or Papa reads to us—he reads very well. Of course, we have guests quite often, or dine out ourselves.'

'And I suppose you play the pianoforte and sing, and read books, and paint pictures, and go to lectures about the poor slaves in Africa, and do charitable work.' Julia sounded distinctly disagreeable.

'I did once hear Mr Wilberforce speak,' Caroline replied equably. 'It wasn't precisely a lecture, though. He was a fellow-guest at dinner, and someone asked him about the slave trade, and his answer was so interesting that everyone stopped talking to listen.'

'And did he convert you?' Mr Hartwell asked, startling Caroline, who had not heard him enter the room.

'Why, no, for I already agreed with him,' she replied.

'Indeed.' Mr Hartwell walked across to a chair near the fire and sat down. He opened the copy of the *Morning Post* which he had brought in with him, and disappeared behind it.

'My godmother has a black boy page,' Julia volunteered at last. 'I believe he is quite happy.'

'I dare say,' Caroline replied, 'but no doubt he is fed and clothed, and not worked very hard. The slaves in the West Indies are a different matter.'

Julia agreed that this was probably so, but without much interest, lapsed into silence, and fidgeted with the trimming on her gown, sighing from time to time, but otherwise contributing nothing to the evening's entertainment.

'Are there any news in the *Post*?' Caroline enquired of the paper barricade after what seemed a long time.

Mr Hartwell lowered the paper and looked at her briefly over it, then raised it again and said, 'Yet another strike in the Manchester mills.'

'What is a strike?' Julia enquired, but without any great interest.

'When the people refuse to work,' Caroline replied, after Mr Hartwell had done nothing but give a faint snort, presumably of exasperation.

'Why do they do that?'

'Probably because they don't think they are paid enough.'

'But if they don't work, they're not paid at all!'

'They hope that the mill-owners will offer them more, rather than have the mills closed.'

'And will the mill-owners do that, do you think?'

'No,' said Mr Hartwell crisply. 'They can't sell what they produce, as things are.'

'What things?'

Mr Hartwell put down his paper and looked hard at his sister, as if he could hardly credit that she was actually seeking information. 'Because the Americans won't buy from us, and we can't send goods into Europe because Bonaparte has closed all the ports to our ships.'

'I thought you said the Americans wouldn't sell us corn. Won't they buy from us either?'

'No. They refuse to trade with anyone involved in the war.'

'Oh. Well, at least they don't buy anything from France either, then.'

'True, but they never did, to any great extent.'

The end of the conversation was signalled by the raising of the news-sheet, and the uncomfortable silence resumed until Caroline tried again.

'Is there no other news?'

'Some rumour of a major victory in Portugal.'

'By whom?' Caroline enquired, as this was by no means clear.

'Arthur Wellesley over Junot. I'd have said "defeat",

had it been otherwise,' Mr Hartwell replied a trifle irritably.

'Portugal?' Julia queried, sounding puzzled.

'Next door to Spain,' he said shortly, and volunteered no further information. The silence resumed.

'Do you play?' Caroline asked, nodding towards the pretty little pianoforte by the window.

'Not very well,' Julia replied, sounding sad. 'I used to have lessons, but my godmother says there's no sense in doing something oneself badly when one can pay someone else to do it well!' She did not invite Caroline to play the instrument, and Caroline, not wishing to put herself forward or give Mr Hartwell another opportunity to criticise his sister, let the matter drop.

The evening continued in this manner for an unconscionably long time, broken only by the arrival of a footman to take the dog for its evening constitutional. Horatio greeted him with affection, and was carried out, rumbling away to himself and industriously licking the footman's cheek, an attention which the man bore stoically.

Soon after that, Mr Hartwell put down his paper and rose to his feet, saying vaguely, 'I have a few matters of business to attend to in the library, if you'll excuse me.' He made Caroline a slight bow, but vouchsafed his half-sister no more than her name and a look, and then he left the room.

Julia sighed, and said, 'I suppose he's right. I should find some useful occupation to pursue in the evenings. To tell truth, I do have a piece of needlework which I started a long time ago, but it's gone wrong, and I don't know how to put it right. Do you think you might know, Cousin Caro?'

'I may do,' Caroline replied. 'Perhaps you could show it to me.'

'Oh, I shall fetch it directly!' Julia jumped up with

more animation than she had shown at any time before. 'I'll not be a minute . . . !' She went off rapidly, although not quite running.

In fact, she was gone for several minutes. Caroline walked about the room, looking at the pictures and ornaments, then picked up the news-sheet and scanned through it. She found the brief report of the strikes in Manchester, but no mention at all of Sir Arthur Wellesley's victory in Portugal, which puzzled her enough to make her sit down on a sofa and go more carefully over the pages to seek for it, but it was not there.

Before she could think of any reason why Mr Hartwell should have mentioned an item of news which was not even reported, Julia returned, clutching a large work-bag made of vivid purple velvet, and a small book. She entered the room swiftly, and came to a halt before Caroline, biting her lip and looking as if she had tensed herself for some ordeal.

'Will you tell me something?' she said abruptly.

'If I can,' Caroline replied equably, wondering what was coming now.

Julia thrust the small book into her hands and replied, 'This is my New Testament. You said you hadn't come to spy on me. Will you swear on that book that you told the truth?'

'If you think it necessary.' Caroline curbed her in-dignation at having her word questioned, and told her-self that this odd girl might have some good reason to suspect that her half-brother might install a spy in the house, for, from her brief acquaintance with Mr Hartwell, she felt that he might well do something of the sort. 'Very well—I swear on this Testament that I have no intention of spying on you. There, will that do? Now, will you show me your needlework?'

Julia looked as if she might dissolve into tears, but

instead she gave a funny little apologetic shrug and shake of the head, and sat down beside Caroline, who unobtrusively laid the Testament on the sofa-table at her elbow before turning to look at the crumpled and grubby piece of linen which Julia pulled out of the work-bag and spread out for her inspection.

It looked as if it might have been intended for a fire-screen, or perhaps a small cushion, with a design of flowers pricked out on it, and a few petals filled in with uneven stitches in pretty soft-coloured silks. The work was poorly done, but the worst part was one leaf, part-filled with a violent green, with overlong stitches which had somehow become pulled up tight so that they formed an ugly cobbled lump.

'You see?' Julian said mournfully, 'I didn't like the colour, so I tried to pull it out, but it wouldn't come!'

'Have you a pair of scissors?' Caroline enquired.

Julia rummaged in the bag and produced a pretty pair shaped like a bird, its long beak forming the blades, and Caroline, pursing her lips judicially, carefully snipped the green silk and pulled out the threads, feeling like Alexander tackling the Gordian knot.

'There,' she said. 'Now, try to make your stitches lie evenly, and go through exactly on the line that's marked. You'll find it slow at first, but you'll improve with practice.'

Julia produced a jumbled tangle of silks, pulled out a long length of a more suitable green, and started to tie a knot in one end of it.

'Oh, no!' Caroline exclaimed. 'No knots! Thread your needle first, and with only a quarter of that length. If you try to use so long a strand, it will tie itself into a tangle.'

The work-bag disgorged a needlecase, a suitable needle was selected, and Julia succeeded eventually in threading it. Then Caroline showed her how to start off, and did a few stitches as an example.

'Put your thimble on, or you'll prick yourself and sleep for a hundred years!' she said jokingly.

'I wish I might,' Julia replied, 'and wake up when everything is different and my handsome prince comes!'

She stitched away slowly and carefully, giving Caroline some hope that she might become a capable needlewoman in time, but it was obvious that, unless distracted, she would soon become bored, so, after a few minutes, Caroline said, 'Why should you think that your brother would set me to spy on you?' She began as she spoke to unravel the tangled silks.

'Because he's so horrid!' Julia replied seriously. 'He's ruined my life and destroyed my happiness, and I'm sure he means to shut me up here until I'm old and grey and dead of boredom!'

'Ruined your life!' Caroline exclaimed. 'But you're not eighteen yet, are you? Whatever did he do that could fill you with despair so young?'

'You mustn't laugh at me,' Julia said defensively. 'He's broken my heart and blighted all my hope of happiness, and there's nothing humorous about that!'

'Indeed, I'm not laughing at you,' Caroline assured her. 'I'd not be so cruel!'

'Robert's cruel,' Julia said despondently. 'I was to be married to the only man in the world I could ever wish for a husband, and Robert put a stop to it and forbade me ever to see him again.'

'Perhaps he thought you too young to be married.' Caroline was surprised to hear herself come perilously near to defending the villain of the piece.

'Not in the least—that didn't enter into it! In fact, it wasn't even mentioned, except that he did say that I couldn't be married without his consent, which isn't even true, for it would be my father's permission I'd need, and I can't get that, with him being in France. Robert isn't my guardian—at least, I don't think he is

. . . Oh, anyway, it wasn't that—it was just that he doesn't like my dear, good Charles!'

'Charles?'

'Sir Charles Corbin. Is it not a fine name?' Julia relished the sound of it, repeating it two or three times in various histrionic styles. 'Oh, Cousin Caro! He is so handsome and kind, so good to me! Anything in the world that I wanted—I had only to name it, and he'd give it to me. He said so, frequently!'

'And Mr Hartwell doesn't like him? Surely he gave some reason?'

'I suppose he may be jealous, for he's not at all handsome or clever or charming, and he looks quite weedy beside my dearest Charles! Robert is mean and dull, always talking of serious, horrid things and discussing politics and how the war is going, and trade and agriculture—nothing in the least interesting or exciting!'

'And what does Sir Charles talk about?' Caroline asked, thinking how like Julia was to her sister Alice, who was always convinced that she would die of boredom if left alone to read a book for half an hour, or of sorrow if her canary escaped.

'Interesting things,' Julia replied vaguely. 'Oh, you know—what Prinny is about at Brighton, the latest *on-dit* from London or Bath, and the fashions, the theatre . . . Oh, everything! He's so full of life and talk, and he dances so divinely! He's a regular out-and-outer —up to all the latest capers! You'd like him, Cousin Caro! Everyone likes him—except Robert.' Her vivacious manner suddenly relapsed into deepest gloom. 'Robert hates him and won't let me see him or write to him, or receive any letters. I'm so miserable!'

'Poor Julia!' Caroline responded sympathetically. 'You must try to put a brave face on it, and perhaps in time your brother may relent if he sees you steadfast in

your affection, and behaving like a grown and respon-
sible young lady.' It seemed a good opportunity to drop
a tactful hint that childish flouncing and sulking were
not likely to convince Mr Hartwell that his half-sister
was capable of a deep and lasting relationship.

'Oh, Robert doesn't care!' Julia stabbed viciously with
her needle, fortunately in the right place in her embroidery. 'I'd like to see how he'd feel if he was barred for ever
from the person he loved most in all the world. But that
will never happen, for it's himself! He'd never do anything so foolish and emotional as fall in love. He has no
sensibilities at all!'

Her strictures were interrupted by the entrance of the
man without sensibilities himself, closely followed by
the servants with tea and a light supper, which, although
it was temptingly set out and looked delicious, Caroline
found herself quite unable to eat, being still over-full
from dinner and lack of exercise.

'Needlework, Julia?' Mr Hartwell observed in a
maddening tone of surprised indulgence. 'Is Cousin
Caroline's good influence already at work?'

Julia's reaction was predictable. She immediately
rolled her work into an untidy bundle and stuffed it into
the purple bag. Caroline continued to untangle the
silks, and, after a few minutes of sulky silence, Julia,
almost absent-mindedly, took up an end of dark red
and began to pursue it through the jumble, winding it
round her fingers.

'Perhaps in the morning, Cousin Caroline,' Mr
Hartwell said mildly, 'you would like to see round the
house? It's quite an interesting building, with a considerable history.'

'I have already planned to show Cousin Caro round
myself,' Julia informed him. 'And in the afternoon, if it's
fine, we shall drive into town and do some shopping.'

'Why do you not walk?' Mr Hartwell asked. 'It's a

pleasant stroll across the fields, and I'm sure the exercise would be good for you both.'

'One may only do things that are good for one in this house,' Julia observed to Caroline in an artificially bright voice.

Caroline looked from one to the other of them, observing Julia's lifted chin and heightened colour, and Mr Hartwell's total lack of expression, save for a set look about his mouth. Could she possible survive a whole month of evenings such as this had been?

'I'm very glad that you agreed to come here, Cousin Caroline,' Mr Hartwell said quietly. 'You'll already have observed how loneliness and boredom have affected Julia's nerves. She used not to be so ill-humoured and shrewish, and I'm sure your company will help her to recover her spirits.'

Caroline hardly knew what to say. She felt that Julia might well erupt into a tantrum to hear herself spoken of in such a patronising fashion, and she was very much inclined to make some sharp rejoinder—possibly even to tell Mr Hartwell what she thought of him, but she was saved from that social solecism by the joyous entry of Horatio, who, having apparently launched himself from a distance at the door, burst it open with a crash and erupted into the room, uttering shrill yelps of excitement and pleasure as he made a rush for Mr Hartwell's boots.

'Ah, Horatio!' that gentleman said mildly, fending the dog off with one foot placed strategically on its chest. 'I gather you had a successful excursion and put the fear of God into the stable rats? Yes, all right then—sit down and tell me quietly! I do wish you would learn to shut doors as well as open them!' (Even as he spoke, a white-gloved hand reached in and silently closed the door.) 'I think, Cousin Caroline, that I omitted to introduce this member of the family to you? This is

Horatio—you may possibly guess the identity of his unwitting godfather? He is, in fact, my dog, in spite of his inclination to attack my boots whenever he sees them. Say how d'you do properly, Horatio!'

The dog sat down suddenly, looked at Caroline, and made some gruff remark which might possibly have been a greeting, or more likely a blank refusal to have anything to do with her.

'How do you do, Horatio,' she said, willing to be friendly. To her surprise, the dog ambled over to her and offered a paw, but before she could lean over and shake it, he fell over, and making the best of it, rolled on his back and presented his stomach to be patted instead.

'There, he likes you too!' Julia observed with satisfaction. 'Now we shall all three get along together very happily, and never mind about Robert in the least, so you may go off on your dull old business, Robert, and we shall do very well without you. Did you warn Cousin Caroline that we're all as moribund as cabbages here, and there is no entertainment whatever, save a long sermon of a Sunday and the occasional passage of a company of soldiers to or from the camp?'

Mr Hartwell's lids drooped over his eyes a little, and he countered this with, 'The powder-mill blows up from time to time, there are occasionally footpads in the Forest, and—oh—I forgot to mention—you are to dine at the Rectory on Monday.'

'At the Rectory! Oh, how thrilling! How can I contain myself! The anticipation!' Julia launched into a dramatic performance worthy of Drury Lane at its worst, then suddenly lapsed into bathos by adding, 'Cousin Caro may do as she pleases, but I shall certainly not go!'

'The invitation has been accepted,' Mr Hartwell said decisively.

'By you, maybe, but you'll be off about your pleasures elsewhere! I shall not endure an evening of total boredom at the Rectory, not under any circumstances. Cousin Caro shall make my excuses and say I have the headache, which will be true, for the mere thought of such an ordeal brings it on!'

Caroline looked at Julia's heightened colour and the defiant tilt of her head, then at the faint signs of a gathering storm on Mr Hartwell's controlled face, for already she could interpret the slight frown between his brows and the tightening of the muscles about his mouth.

'I think,' she said dispassionately, 'that it might be well for both of us to go. It will make a change for you, even if only of one boredom for another, and you never know—you might have a pleasant surprise!'

Mr Hartwell kept a discreet silence, and Julia, after a startled stare at her cousin, said reluctantly, 'Oh, well —if you wish to go—I dare say it will be a change from sitting about here, and perhaps Mrs Calvert will have invited some of the officers from the camp . . .' She brightened considerably at that thought, and had soon talked herself into deciding to go to the Rectory dinner after all, but only for Cousin Caro's sake.

Soon after this, to Caroline's relief, it was time to retire. She lay awake for some time, wondering if she should seek an interview with Mr Hartwell in the morning and tell him that she wished to go home, or whether it would be better to wait a few days, at least until he returned from wherever he was going on Monday, in the hope that matters would improve once he was out of the way.

It was not just the prospect of a very dull month which worried her, but more the atmosphere of hostility between Julia and her half-brother, and the girl's mercurial behaviour. She felt torn between a desire to help her cousin, and an equal desire to flee home to the harmony and happiness of her own family, and her dilemma was still unresolved when she fell asleep.

CHAPTER
FOUR

CAROLINE WOKE very early in the morning, before there was any sign that anyone else was stirring, although, presumably, the servants were about to get up, for she heard the distant sound of the 'prentice bell ringing across the fields from the church. Below her window, the early morning sun cast long shadows down the garden, and the fields in the valley were wreathed in mist, which she thought vaguely might betoken another fine day ahead.

After fidgeting about the room for a time, discovering where Martha had hidden her belongings, she made a sudden decision to find her way outside and walk about the garden to clear her head and help her decide what to do, for her problem was still far from resolved. She washed with the remains of last night's water-can, dressed, took one of her shawls against the morning chill, and slipped quietly out of her room, then paused to listen for any sound of movement in the house.

As she stood listening, her eye fell on a small brass knob in the wainscoting of the passage wall, and she bent to look more closely at it, then took hold of it and tried it, for it looked for all the world like the door-knob of a closet.

Sure enough, the knob turned and a door opened in the panelling, revealing not a closet, but the top of a flight of steps concealed in the thickness of the wall, which must be one of the outer walls of the house, for a little slit of a window was cut half-way down to give enough light for a safe descent of the steps.

Prudently, Caroline made sure that there was another

knob on the inside of the door before she closed it and cautiously descended. The window was partly overgrown with ivy, she discovered when she reached it, and she could see very little from it—only leaves and a branch of a large tree, from which a white dove was surveying the morning.

At the foot of the stairs there was not enough light to see if there was a door, so Caroline felt the outer wall at about the level where a knob might be, but found only rough stone, so she tried the inner wall, and immediately her hand encountered another knob of the same family as the two upstairs. The door opened stiffly, as if it was seldom used, the hinges creaking a little, and she stepped out into a very handsome library, closing the door behind her.

It was a large room, about the same size as the dining-room, which a little consideration led her to believe must be next door, and, judging by the view from the windows across the front terrace to the garden, her own bedroom must be above at least part of it. The walls were lined with open bookshelves filled with a variety of volumes, mostly well bound and with gold tooling on the backs, but one bay was entirely filled with ordinary bindings, such as would come directly from a book-shop, and a quick survey of the titles revealed that they were all novels of the more popular sort, although none very recently published.

Greatly cheered by this discovery, Caroline walked about looking at the titles on other shelves, and at the furniture about the room. There was a large terrestrial globe and a celestial partner to it in a pair of alcoves on either side of the door, one of the sort of library ladder which turns itself into a reading-chair, several large, well-worn, comfortable-looking armchairs, and a few small glass-topped tables containing curios and bibelots. A very large leather-topped desk stood across the central of the three windows. On it was a pile of papers, and a curious-looking object which Caroline could not identify until she went to examine it more closely, and then she discovered that it was a sort of writer's *nécessaire*, a hexagonal box revolving on a spindle, which was set on a heavy base. Each of the sides had a door which opened to reveal various sizes of paper, a set of equipment for sealing, a selection of pens, an inkwell, and a small pistol, which she did not think was part of the original contents.

Having satisfied her curiosity, she fastened the little door-latches, twirled the box on its spindle a couple of times, and was turning away from the desk when she happened to glance at the top sheet of the pile of papers and saw written on it, 'Ask Barnes about ships.'

Had her own surname not appeared on the paper, she would not have looked any further, for she was a well-brought-up young lady, not given to reading things which did not concern her, even if this was not precisely a letter or anything of that nature, but she wondered if 'Barnes' might refer to her father, who certainly knew about ships—East Indiamen, at least—so she ran her eye down the rest of the sheet to see if there was anything to confirm or deny her surmise.

It appeared to be a shopping-list of sorts, for it said, 'Hay. Oats. Harness. Wagons—can country ones be obtained? Draught beasts also? Gold.' The last was underlined several times, and seemed not to have any connection with the other things. Caroline read the list two or three times and puzzled over it, then wondered if Mr Hartwell might be engaged in trade of some sort.

Yes, of course! That must be it! That was why he was reluctant to talk about his travels, for it was much beneath the dignity of a member of the Landed Gentry to engage in trade. Why, he had actually mentioned sordid haggling, and the price of corn!

Pensively, she wandered away from the desk, pursuing the line of thought which this discovery had opened up. He had mentioned something to her mother about the cost of receiving and sending letters to his father, and had he not said something yesterday at dinner about the family having only one other estate, and that let? Most of the furniture in the house—or, at least, those parts she had seen—was old and well worn . . . Perhaps Mr Hartwell was short of money, and seeking for some way to get more. Perhaps he wouldn't let Julia marry because he had no money for her dowry! Perhaps . . .

These interesting speculations were interrupted by the sudden entry into the room of Mr Hartwell himself, looking both purposeful and preoccupied to the extent that he was well into the room before he noticed that someone was present. He stopped dead in mid-stride and looked at her for a moment with an odd expression on his face, then smiled a little and said, 'Good morning, Cousin Caroline. So you're an early riser? I hope you can persuade Julia to follow your example.'

'Good morning, Mr Hartwell,' Caroline replied a trifle formally. 'I was admiring your library.' She was both embarrassed at being caught demonstrating a possibly ill-bred curiosity about her surroundings, and miffed by his assumption of a relationship to her which did not exist.

'No more mine than anything else here, as Julia is so fond of pointing out. Ours, perhaps. Do you like to read?'

'Very much.'

'Then, pray, feel free to borrow any books you please, but on one small condition—that you replace each volume in the place where you found it. My father catalogued the collection shortly before he—he left us, and I should like him to find everything in its place when he returns.'

'Certainly.' Caroline, who was tidy-minded, felt a mild irritation at being instructed to do as she would have done as a matter of course. 'Thank you. There seems to be a very wide choice here—everything from the very old to quite recent novels.'

'Indeed. Some of the very old volumes come from the Abbey, according to the inscriptions inside them. Several of them contain a Latin curse on anyone who misappropriates them, but I believe our ancestor, who was the last steward of the Abbey before the Dissolution, must have come by them legitimately.'

An awkward silence ensued, and Mr Hartwell simply stood looking at her, while she tried to avoid his gaze while thinking of something to say.

'I—er—I suppose Martha will wonder where I am . . . ,' she said at last, then realised that she had no idea of how to return to her room except by the way she had come, and she felt reluctant to admit that she had been so curious as to open a door merely to discover what was behind it, or to descend a 'secret' staircase just to find out where it led.

'I expect she'll realise that you are already come down,' Mr Hartwell replied. 'Shall I show you a little of the house until breakfast is served? We have half an hour or so . . .'

'But are you not busy?'

'Not particularly—nothing that cannot wait.' Apparently assuming that she had voiced her only re-servation about his suggestion, he gestured about him, and went on, 'This, as you may have guessed, is the oldest part of the house, and was built in the fourteenth century, we believe, for the stewards of the Abbey, who had charge of the business affairs of the Abbey, and also of its home farm, or grange—hence the name. This and the dining-room next door were originally the Great Hall, which was divided by panelling in the seventeenth century to make the two rooms, and your room and the one next to it were made in the roof-space at about the same time. The entrance hall, the parlour, and the rooms above them were added in the sixteenth century, just after the Dissolution, when the first Hartwell here bought the house from King Henry.'

'What became of the steward then?' asked Caroline with genuine interest.

'His name was Cressy, and his only child, a daughter, married Matthew Hartwell, and so contrived to keep his old roof over her father's head. We are descended from that marriage.'

Caroline responded in a proper fashion, and went with him out of the library and along a dark passage to the entrance hall, where he pointed out various odd features, such as the sudden change of floor level where a seventeenth-century Hartwell built on a brick wing extending back from the parlour side of the house to provide a music-room, a small dining-room, and various domestic offices, leaving an awkward step on which most of his descendants had contrived to trip up or down ever since.

It was all very interesting, for she had never before been in a house which had grown over several centuries, with successive generations building on or knocking down to suit their current needs. The result, she thought, was something of a labyrinth, and she was soon quite lost as they moved along passages and looked into rooms of various sizes and uses, several of which had their contents shrouded in dust-sheets. She was quite surprised when they turned a corner and emerged into the entrance hall through a door under the stairs which she had not noticed before.

'I hope I haven't bored you?' Mr Hartwell enquired, sounding as if he did not expect an affirmative answer. 'I'm sure, however, that you must be more than ready for your breakfast, so shall we . . . ?' And he conducted her along a corridor hung with pictures to a pleasant breakfast-room which looked out from the south-east front of the building along the side of the ridge on which it was built, and so was bright with the morning sunshine.

It was a pretty room, reflecting, Caroline thought, a more feminine taste than most of the rooms she had seen during her tour. An oval table of reasonable size for half a dozen people occupied the middle of it, with a snowy cloth set ready with silver flatware and some very attractive floral china. Opposite the windows, a long sideboard supported an array of chafing-dishes which exuded pleasant odours of bacon, toast, hot fresh bread, mushrooms, and other less readily identifiable foods. The dog Horatio was sitting upright on a chair facing the door, his head just showing over the edge of the table, looking for all the world like an old gentleman waiting for someone to serve him with a plate of cutlets and a dish of coffee.

'That,' observed Mr Hartwell, 'is not *de règle*. You will be relieved to hear, Cousin Caroline, that the dog does not sit at table with us! Down, Horatio, and out!'

The dog got down, grumbling, and went out, pausing to wag its tail hopefully at Caroline, who bade it 'Good morning', and to growl in passing at Mr Hartwell's boots, as if promising them a proper sorting-out later.

Julia arrived while Caroline was still deciding between the respective merits of bacon, kedgeree, cutlets or cold ham, hot rolls or toast, and tea or coffee, and demurely bade both cousin and brother 'Good morning' before toying delicately with a piece of dry toast and a dish of weak tea.

'I apprehend that you're going into a decline again, Julia,' Mr Hartwell commented with a jaundiced glance at her frugal breakfast.

'You wouldn't care overmuch if I did,' she returned coldly.

'Oh, I think I might manage to feel some slight concern,' her brother replied calmly. 'Perhaps, if you feel up to it, you will make a note of your last wishes, and I'll probably do something about them when I'm less occupied.'

'You mean that you'd actually carry them out?' Julia sounded incredulous.

'Probably not,' he admitted with a marked lack of concern.

'I have only one wish,' Julia said primly, 'and that is to marry my dear Charles.'

'Ah, yes—dear Charles . . .' Mr Hartwell transferred his attention to Caroline. 'I suppose Julia has told you about dear Charles? Did she tell you that I found her in the course of eloping with him? I thought not!'

Caroline had not replied to his question, but she could not check a startled glance at Julia at the mention of elopement, which, of course, he interpreted correctly.

'Did she tell you the nature of my objections to the marriage?' he went on.

'I don't choose to repeat your wicked and unfounded libels on the best man in the world,' Julia declared grandly.

'Slander, my dear, not libel! It was said, not written! One of these days, you'll appreciate that you owe me some thanks for intervening! However . . . perhaps you would care to show Cousin Caroline round the upper part of the house when you've finished mangling that inoffensive slice of toast . . . and the gardens and yards as well, if she would care to see them? I have to go over to Pinnacles this morning, but I'll be back for luncheon.'

'Pinnacles? But Lord Cressing is away, is he not?'
Julia was diverted into enquiring.

'He and Lady Cressing are due to return this morning. 'If you'll excuse me . . .' He rose, giving Caroline
an unexpectedly attractive smile before he left the
room.

Once the door had closed behind him, Julia pushed
her plate of crumbled toast away and went to the sideboard to serve herself a proper breakfast, which she
consumed with good appetite, making no mention of her
brother's surprising revelation, but telling Caroline what
she intended showing her in the house and grounds,
which she proceeded to do as soon as breakfast was
finished.

By luncheon-time, Caroline had been taken all over
the first floor of the house and briefly shown all the
bedrooms, closets, broom-cupboards and store-rooms,
but not, she was thankful to find, the attics or the
servants' rooms on the floor above.

The principal bedrooms were an interesting set of
contrasts, Julia's being pretty but predictably untidy, her
mother's very feminine, but over-crowded with knick-
knacks and elaborations, and her sister's still the room of
a child, with favourite toys lying as she had left them,
pathetic symbols of a childhood passing in captivity
which brought a moment's thoughtful and melancholy
pause in the progress of the two cousins.

Sir William's room was luxuriously antique, with very
fine old furniture, all well cared for, but Caroline felt
certain there was nothing there less than a century old,
and Mr Hartwell's, by contrast, quite austere. His bed
was a plain wooden one without hangings, and all the
other furniture was so plain that it took a second look to
see that it was of excellent design and workmanship,
although, as in his father's room, there was nothing new.
Nor was there anything very personal, except a riding-

crop left on a chair and a small, battered wooden horse on the window-sill.

'The monk's cell,' was Julia's sole comment on it, and Caroline, with an unaccountable drop in her spirits, thought that was a good description, for it certainly seemed the room of a man with no desire for worldly attachments—except for the toy horse . . .

'Come and see the schoolroom,' Julia said impatiently as Caroline lingered in the doorway. 'We had some grand times there before Mary went away.' She then led the way towards the back of the house, to a corner room with windows looking in two directions, one on the stableyard and the other on a rose-garden.

Apart from a couple of ink-stained desks, each with a chair designed to improve the deportment of the young lady who might use it, the schoolroom looked more like a sitting-room. A loo table was set under one window, with four shabby, comfortable chairs round it, and there were old cretonne-covered chairs by the large fireplace with its high spark-guard to protect the rag rug on the floor. The room was particularly well supplied with cupboards, which Julia opened to reveal an assortment of toys and games, some of them so old and battered that Caroline wondered how many generations of children had played with them, and others quite new, looking as though they had never been used at all.

'This was Robert's,' Julia said suddenly, picking up a toy which had fallen from one of the cupboards as she opened the door. It was a small ladder with a jointed figure of a sailor fastened to it in such a way that it could be made to turn somersaults if one squeezed the sides of the ladder. Several of the rungs were broken, and the figure had lost a leg. 'He used to let me play with it when I was little, as a special treat, but I broke it!' She frowned and bit her lip. 'I remember I cried and hid under the bed because I was ashamed to tell him, but he came and found me, and he was very kind and said it didn't matter. Isn't it odd, when he's so horrid now?'

'People change as they grow up,' Caroline observed absently, for she was more interested in collecting together several games which might suitably be played of an evening by two young ladies with nothing better to do. Julia welcomed the idea when she suggested it to her, and they quickly shut the doors on the toys and took the games to the parlour, where room was soon found for the various cards, pieces and dice in a little games table which contained nothing but half an old pack of cards.

There was no time before luncheon for more than a very cursory look at the gardens, and after the meal, which was taken in a slightly more informal style than dinner the previous night, Julia ordered the carriage to be brought round for their expedition into the town.

Caroline was a little surprised that Mr Hartwell made no objection to their driving instead or walking, and more so when he joined them in the vehicle just as they were setting off.

'Are you coming?' Julia exclaimed with a marked lack of enthusiasm.

'If I may be permitted to go where I please in my own carriage,' he replied drily. 'I have a bill to settle at the blacksmith's.'

'Doesn't Mr Howard see to all the bills?' Julia enquired, with an aside to Caroline that Mr Howard was the estate steward. 'I'm sure he said the other day that he'd settled them all for last month.'

Mr Hartwell raised his eyebrows, as if surprised that Julia had taken notice of so mundane a matter, and replied that it was a private bill, and nothing to do with the estate.

'Oh!' Julia said comprehendingly. 'One of those! Will Somers, the blacksmith, is a local villain, you know,

Cousin Caro! Most of the gentlemen about here receive large bills from him for inordinate numbers of hinges and horseshoes—and some of the ladies as well!'

Caroline must have looked as blank as she felt, for she could not imagine what Julia meant, but Mr Hartwell kindly enlightened her by saying, 'He's the captain of the local nighthawks—smugglers—and, incidentally, of the bell-ringers.'

During this exchange, the carriage had descended the winding drive to the road, and set off at a brisk pace back along the way by which Caroline had arrived, until it reached the end of the town, where it turned right into East Street. Caroline thought it quaint and attractive, particularly as it had an inexplicable dog-leg half-way along, which seemed to add to its character. It debouched into one corner of a market square full of stalls, with people noisily buying and selling, and the carriage stopped outside an inn which occupied most of the northern side of the square. It was as odd a building as Caroline had ever seen, for its great black timbers leaned drunkenly to one side, and there was not a horizontal or vertical one among them.

At the far end of the inn, which sported a large sign painted with a bell, there was an archway between it and the next building, a primly upright little clap-boarded house, which seemed to be unwillingly supporting its drunken neighbour. Through the arch, Caroline caught a glimpse of the churchyard as she descended from the carriage.

'I'll attend to my business, then come and find you somewhere about the market,' Mr Hartwell said briefly, and went to speak to the coachman, who then set the carriage in motion down another street which continued the line of East Street downhill alongside the churchyard wall.

'Oh, very well,' his sister replied ungraciously, but he

had already gone in the wake of the carriage. 'Now, Cousin Caro, let me see if I can match this ribbon. I'm sure there'll be a stall here somewhere with haber-dashery.' Plunging into the crowd about the stalls with-out more ado, she left Caroline to follow the blue flowers in her bonnet as best she could.

There were, in fact, three stalls selling ribbons, laces and pins and needles, amid the vegetables, leather goods, fabrics, butter and eggs, live chickens and dead rabbits which seemed to fill most of the others, and Julia, with Caroline at hand for a second opinion, tried her yellow ribbon against those on offer at all three, but was not well satisfied with any.

'Oh, I don't know!' she exclaimed at last. 'I think perhaps, after all, the one on the first stall was the best match. I'll just run back and get it. Do you stay here —I'll not be a minute!' She sped off, dodging between housewives, children and idlers and out of sight round a barrow piled high with pairs of rough working-boots.

Caroline drew back from the bustle and stood against the wall of one of the five inns which stood about the market square, watching with some interest, for she had not visited a country market before, and became so absorbed in the bargaining between a trader and a would-be customer over a particularly hideous jug that she was considerably startled when a pleasant voice said from close beside her, 'Good day, Miss Barnes! I trust you are well, and enjoying your stay at Woodham?'

She looked up into the face of a total stranger, a tall, broad-shouldered man with very fair wavy hair, a hand-some face with friendly brown eyes and dark brows, and a very charming smile.

'We almost met yesterday afternoon,' he prompted. 'You were sitting in Hartwell's chaise outside his old nurse's cottage.'

'Oh, yes,' Caroline replied uncertainly, recalling the

man on horseback who had stopped and bowed to her. 'But I think we are not acquainted, sir.'

'Social matters are very informal in the country,' he replied easily. 'And everyone knows that Hartwell has brought a cousin from London to keep company with Miss Hartwell. Bramwell Bell, ma'am, at your service! I trust we shall meet again before long,' and he bowed in an elegant manner, replaced his grey beaver at a jaunty angle, and sauntered off, disappearing into the crowd before Caroline could reply.

At that moment, a dog-fight broke out near by, two terriers having taken a violent dislike to one another for some reason, and the struggling bodies succeeded in knocking over a pile of plates on the pottery stall. By the time the owners of the combatants had finished shouting at each other and the dogs, a woman had come out of the inn behind Caroline and thrown a bucket of water over dogs and bystanders impartially, and the broken plates had been argued over and paid for, Caroline had almost forgotten about Mr Bell, and Julia's return, with the suggestion of a visit to the milliner's in East Street, put him out of her head altogether.

The milliner kept a surprisingly large stock for a small town, and the two young ladies spent a pleasant half-hour trying on the more fashionable models. Julia could not take a liking to any of the bonnets or hats on offer, but Caroline, whose father had given her a comfortably fat purse to bring with her, bought a dashing jockey-cap which she thought would be just the thing for country walks.

By the time she and Julia returned to the market square, it was clear to Caroline that Mr Hartwell had been awaiting them for some time, although he was doing nothing but stand outside the Bell with a marked lack of expression on his face.

'Ah, there you are, Robert!' Julia said airily, as if he

had just arrived and she had been waiting. 'Where is the
carriage to meet us?'

'Nowhere. Henry took it straight home after he left
us,' Mr Hartwell replied coolly.

'But did he not drive down Church Street to the
Swan?'

'No, only to turn round outside the church, where
there's more room. We shall walk home across the
fields.'

Caroline eyed Mr Hartwell's face, expecting to see a
gleam of triumph or satisfaction there at having out-
witted his sister, but he met her scrutiny with a look of
limpid innocence which quite disconcerted her—an unexpected feeling, which increased when he gave her a
faint, wry smile, to which she could not help but respond, although she had no wish to do so, for she
thought he had played a petty trick on Julia.

On the other hand, she was far from displeased herself
by the prospect of walking, for it was a form of exercise
which she much enjoyed, albeit usually in the streets
of the City or suburban Stepney, and she willingly
accompanied Mr Hartwell across the churchyard,
pausing to marvel at the great size of the church, and
observe the broken wall at the east end, where the choir
and presbytery of the canons had been pulled down,
leaving the truncated nave. Their path passed through
what had once been the base of the central tower of the
great church, through a gate in a wall built, Mr Hartwell
said, on the foundations of the north wall of the choir,
and across the former cloister garth.

'I thought that cloisters were always on the south
side,' Caroline remarked.

'They are usually, but I suppose the churchyard was
already to the south, for the canons built on to an
existing church,' he replied, unlocking another gate in
the far corner of the cloisters and standing aside to

let Caroline and a sulky Julia pass through before him.

Caroline was surprised to find that they were in an orchard, where a man and two boys were picking apples. They greeted Mr and Miss Hartwell by name, and one of the boys brought his basket over to offer a taste of the fruit. Julia declined, although with an effort at politeness, but her brother recommended the russets to Caroline, and she took one and found it sweet and crisp, with a flavour of cinnamon. Mr Hartwell quite spoiled the line of his coat by putting half a dozen in his pockets as well as taking one to eat, and Caroline noticed that he dropped a silver coin into the basket as he thanked the boy.

'The manor house used to stand here.' Mr Hartwell gestured vaguely with his bitten apple as they went on. 'It burned down about a century ago, and the Lord of the Manor didn't bother to rebuild as his principal residence is in the Midlands. The Abbey's domestic buildings probably stood here before that—bakeries and brewhouses and so forth.'

When they emerged from the orchard (again through a locked gate, which made Caroline wonder how Mr Hartwell came to have the keys to all these gates), they crossed a field and then followed the bank of a small stream overhung by willows and busy with ducks. Mr Hartwell said that this was the Cornmill stream, the same which flowed in front of the church, which Caroline did not quite understand at the time. Julia lagged behind, ostentatiously hesitating and making a wide detour at the few slightly muddy patches they encountered. Mr Hartwell usually took a long stride over them, then turned to give a hand to Caroline so that she might jump over. She was surprised to find that each time he held on to her hand a shade longer than was strictly necessary, and quite frequently smiled at her in a friendly fashion, which made her self-conscious, and a little uneasy.

There were no horned beasts or other horrors along the bank of the stream, only some pigs, which were happily standing half-way up their fat sides in the water, eating the weed which streamed in the current.

'I didn't know that pigs ever went into water!' Caroline exclaimed.

'Quite often,' Mr Hartwell replied. 'Contrary to popular belief, they swim well, and don't cut their own throats with their trotters while doing so. Apple sauce!' he called in greeting, and the pigs replied with a chorus of grunts.

Caroline could not help laughing, but Julia cried, 'Robert! How cruel!' in a very prim tone.

After a mile or so, the path turned away from the stream and skirted the edges of a couple of arable fields full of some green crop which Mr Hartwell said was turnips, and then passed through a wood in which Caroline was made a little nervous by stirrings and rustlings in the undergrowth which the other two did not seem to hear.

'I believe there is something or someone over there,' she said, pointing.

'Provided whoever it is ain't taking my game-birds, I'm not much concerned,' Mr Hartwell replied loudly. 'Is that you, Warrener?'

'It be, Mester 'Artwell,' replied a voice from somewhere amid the thickets. 'I be netting a couple or so o' your bucks to put to my does, and I be putting two o' my best bucks in their place. Yore kipper knows.'

'Ah, yes! Thank you. Good day to you, then!' Mr Hartwell replied, and added for Caroline's edification, 'Warrener follows the profession of his ancestors, and attends to the rabbits on the Pinnacles estate, which belongs to Lord Cressing. He's doing a little crossbreeding to put some fresh blood into his charges, and mine at the same time.' He did not explain what a 'kipper' might be, but Caroline concluded that it was unlikely to be a smoked herring.

'I thought rabbits were considered to be pests!' Caroline exclaimed.

'They're an important source of food to the poor people, and fur besides,' Mr Hartwell replied. 'They need to be controlled, though, or they do become pests, eating grass and crops that should feed beasts and people.'

'Oh, do come on!' Julia exclaimed petulantly. 'We've all the uphill part to go yet.'

CHAPTER
FIVE

JULIA'S FIT of sulks lasted until after dinner, but her mood improved after the meal when she and Caroline had sat for a while with their needlework and she had given vent to her feelings concerning Robert's unkindness in making her do something which she disliked so much as walking in the country. Caroline commented only that exercise in the fresh air was beneficial to both the figure and the complexion, and praised her for the improvement in her stitchery, for she was clearly taking pains with it.

Mr Hartwell appeared briefly with confirmation of Sir Arthur Wellesley's victory at Talavera, bringing an atlas with him so that the ladies might find out where it was, but he did not linger, so the evening passed more pleasantly for Caroline than she had expected.

In the morning, there was another small scene at breakfast over attending Matins, for Julia declared rebelliously that her godmother never attended church, but she did not seem to have much expectation of winning this battle, and capitulated with only a few shrugs and pouts when Caroline said that she always attended when at home, and would like very much to go to service in such an interesting old building.

The church surprised her, for she had somehow expected it to be much like her own familiar St Dunstan's with its elegant slim pillars and soaring gothic arches, but Woodham's church was altogether more massive and much older. Its pillars and columns were like vast tree-trunks of stone, its arches rounded and heavy, rising in three great tiers to a wooden ceiling nearly sixty feet above her head, and most of its windows were small and plain; yet, oddly enough, it was not dark and forbidding, for the high clerestory windows admitted a flood of sunlight, and the stone walls, which were not plastered and whitewashed like those of her own parish church, were a pale golden stone which seemed to glow with a warm light of its own. The only jarring note was struck by the east end, for, behind the altar, where there should have been a big, colourful window, she felt, glowing like a great jewel, there was only a rough stone wall pierced by a mean, rectangular window of dull greenish glass, with two dark paintings below it, representing (according to Mr Hartwell) Moses and Aaron, but they were so dim with age and dirty varnish that they might have been anyone.

'What do you think of it?' he enquired in a suitably subdued voice as they sat in the Canons Grange pew waiting for the service to start.

'It's very grand and glorious, but for the east end,' Caroline whispered back. 'I suppose that is where the rest of the church was broken off.'

'Yes. The townspeople were able to prove that this had always been their parish church, so they were allowed to keep it, but the Abbey was the main source of employment for the town, and, with that gone, they were too poor to do any more than fill up the gap where the canons' part had been pulled down with whatever came to hand.' He was unable to say more, for a small band in the west gallery struck up the Introit and everyone rose to sing heartily, if not always tunefully, as the service began.

The familiar words of the Prayer Book were a comfort to Caroline, who was still feeling cut off from her happy home, and very much set down amid the alien corn. She took a liking to the clergy as well—Mr Jones the Curate, with a slight Welsh melodiousness in his voice, and the

Rector, Mr Calvert, who was a stoutish middle-aged gentleman with an engaging air of mild eccentricity. He preached the sermon, gazing benignly from time to time at his congregation through a pair of steel-rimmed spectacles, and generally losing his place in his sheaf of notes for a few moments after doing so.

Like any young lady of marriageable age but no immediate prospect of changing her condition, Caroline noted that both the pews in the chancel were occupied, the lesser one by a dark-haired young lady with a merry brown face—presumably the Curate's wife—and the grander one by a thin, much beshawled lady who looked as if she might suffer from ill-health.

After the service, several groups of people stood out talking in the large porch in the base of the west tower, and outside on the paved area before the door, and Mr Hartwell took the trouble to make some of them known to Caroline, but she hardly comprehended whom any of them were, apart from Mr Calvert. He made her a pleasant little speech of welcome and said that he was pleased to know that she and Miss Hartwell were to dine at the Rectory the next evening.

'I hope my daughter Lucinda may be home by then,' he added. 'She and her husband were expected home from Bath yesterday, but they've been delayed in London and will make the last part of their journey tomorrow. I don't think she has had the pleasure of Miss Hartwell's acquaintance yet, and I'm sure you young people will get along famously.'

To judge by the lowering expression on Julia's face as she walked off without replying, this seemed unlikely, in her case at least, but Caroline's spirits lifted a little at the thought of finding some congenial society to relieve the burden of Julia's temperamental companionship. She told Mr Calvert that she very much looked forward to eating her mutton with him and meeting his daughter, and then gave place to a faintly plaintive elderly lady who was waiting impatiently to confide some domestic disaster to the Rector's sympathetic ear.

Caroline moved away and looked about her for Mr Hartwell, but he was engaged in conversation with a grey-haired army officer in full regimentals, and, to judge by his gold braid, of fairly high rank. Julia seemed to have disappeared altogether, and it was a few moments before she located her.

The forecourt of the church extended for several yards before the building, and there was then an area of roadway to allow carriage access to the building and the Rectory beside it on Caroline's right. Beyond the road-way was a stream which emerged from under a large clap-boarded mill building beyond the Rectory and flowed across towards her left. The main street came down by the churchyard wall from the market square and plunged into the stream at the bottom, emerging on the other side, apparently as West Street, to continue between more shops and houses towards the powder-mill, the marshes of the main river, and so into the next county. Between the ford and the mill, a wooden footbridge crossed the stream, and it was there that Caroline eventually saw Julia, leaning on the hand-rail and engaged in animated conversation with a tall, dark army officer.

For one brief moment, Caroline wondered if this could be 'dearest Charles', but then she recollected that there had been no mention of his being in uniform, and, in view of Julia's outspoken admiration for a red coat, this was surely something she would not have omitted if it applied. She also recollected that Mr Hartwell had forbidden Julia to communicate with her beloved, and, as he was standing in clear view of his sister, yet not showing any signs of anger, she could only conclude that this was not Sir Charles Corbin. Nevertheless, Julia's absorption in the officer was a little too thorough for propriety, so Caroline, although reluctant to appear interfering, thought it best to walk over to the bridge and join them.

'Oh, Cousin Caro! Let me present to you Captain —no, *Major*—Bridges, who is second in command of the army camp just up the valley. My cousin, Miss Barnes, from London. The poor Major is just come back from sick leave after being wounded in Sweden.'

'Sweden?' Caroline queried after exchanging greetings with the Major, who was, quite simply, the handsomest man she had ever seen in the flesh, being six feet of lean, exquisitely-tailored perfection in his immaculate uniform, with a classic profile and a fine head of thick and sufficiently curly dark hair. His manners were as perfect as his appearance, his voice was pleasant, and he gave the impression of most sincere attention to both his present companions. No wonder that even love-lorn Julia was pleased to see him!

'It would be more accurate to say *off* Sweden,' he replied, smiling and revealing teeth of surpassing whiteness and evenness. 'We were sent there in the spring to assist the Swedes, but they wouldn't even let us land! That's what comes of having a mad king, I suppose . . .' He broke off suddenly, and his healthily bronzed face reddened in an endearingly boyish fashion as he realised what he had said.

'Unless he happens to be a British king, of course,' observed Mr Hartwell, who had joined them unnoticed, 'and then it hardly matters, except that one feels great sympathy for poor old Farmer George and his family. Pray, James, how did you come to be wounded by our eccentric allies if you were not let ashore?'

'Even a musket-ball travels a fair distance,' the Major replied, 'and we were in harbour at Gothenburg, only a few yards out from the quay. To be fair, I don't think the fellow at the other end of it was actually aiming at me, but he ruined my coat and made a hole in my upper arm—the left one, luckily. It's taken a while to heal. I say—I gather that we all dine together at the Rectory tomorrow?'

'Not I, I'm afraid,' Mr Hartwell said, sounding regretful. 'I shall be away in the morning for a few days.'

Major Bridges gave him a sharp look, but made no comment, and after a little more conversation, he excused himself, made his bows, or more accurately salutes, and marched himself off.

'Tell me, Cousin Caroline,' Mr Hartwell said thoughtfully as he strolled across to the waiting carriage beside her, 'why is it that every female between six and sixty finds a red coat so overpoweringly attractive?'

'I was not aware that there's any age-limit,' she replied evasively, 'for I know two or three ladies who might admit to being past sixty who would still smile upon Major Bridges, given the opportunity!'

Mr Hartwell gave her a considering look, and his lips twitched in a smile of pure amusement. 'I do believe, Cousin Caroline, that there is a great deal more to you than at first appears. How do you propose to amuse yourself and dear Julia in my absence?'

'If the weather holds, I should like to explore a little,' she replied, 'and perhaps do some sketching. There must be some pleasant views from the higher ground behind the house.'

'And if it rains?'

'You have kindly made me free of your library, and you have a pianoforte.'

'Julia seldom reads and never plays.'

'There is a difference between doing something alone and doing it with a companion.'

At that point they reached the carriage, where Julia,

who had walked on ahead of them, had already taken
her place, apparently determined to be in the vehicle
before her brother could dismiss it and force her to walk
home again, but he made no demur about riding home.
This was as well, as they reached Canons Grange with
barely time to tidy themselves before luncheon.

Caroline persuaded Julia to walk with her to the
poplar on the top of the ridge during the afternoon, and
from there, having admired the view, back by a more
circuitous path, and, somehow, by the time she retired
that night after a lively game of cards with her cousin,
Caroline had forgotten that she had intended to tell Mr
Hartwell that she wished to return home.

He left Woodham very early the next morning, before
either of the young ladies was up, and the atmosphere, in
the abovestairs part of the house at least, was the lighter
for his absence. Julia seemed better tempered and more
willing to pursue some activity when safe from her
brother's critical eye and acid tongue, and even
appeared to view the prospect of dinner at the Rectory
with some equanimity.

In the event, the evening was a great success. Caroline
suggested going up to dress rather earlier than seemed
strictly necessary, so that both ladies were ready in good
time, Caroline in a soft rose-coloured silk with a necklace of amethysts set in silver, lent by her mother, and
amethyst-coloured ribbons in her hair, and Julia demure
in cream barège over a green underdress, with a simple
string of pearls round her neck and a pearl ornament
among her curls.

The party at the Rectory was of medium size, with six
couples sitting down to dinner, and Caroline was pleased
to see that Major Bridges was among the guests, particularly as he sat next to Julia and occupied her attention
sufficiently to prevent her becoming bored, and, Caroline feared, possibly less than well-mannered. She her-

self was paired, to her surprise, with a real Viscount, albeit only a honorary one as he was the eldest son of an Earl. He proved to be the Rector's good-son, being married to Mr Calvert's daughter Lucinda.

The other guests were Mr Jones the Curate, his wife Amaryllis (called Amy by most of the company), a mouse-like little lady of uncertain age called Miss Enstone, whose sharp little eyes and ears were constantly on the alert for every scrap of news, Colonel Long, the camp commandant, and another officer, Captain Marsh. A thirteenth person was also unfortunately found to be present, concealed under the table. It was Frederick, the Rectory cat, a large black and white animal of amiable disposition but ferocious reputation in the rodent world, who was quite prepared to accept titbits from anyone who would offer them, and generally contribute to the success of the evening in his own inimitable fashion.

'Superstition, of course, has no place at the Rectory dining-table,' Mrs Calvert said firmly from the foot of the table when the thirteenth presence was detected. 'Nevertheless, I am mortified that this should have happened!'

'But does an animal count?' enquired Marsh, a personable young man who might have been thought handsome had Major Bridges not been present.

'Fred does, in his own estimation, at least,' Lucinda replied, her face alight with amusement. She was not, Caroline had decided, a Beauty, but she had pleasing features, a lively face, and very pleasant manners.

'Oh, if anyone's worried, look you,' Mr Jones said gravely, 'they may rest easy, for we are fourteen, in fact! Are we not, Amy?'

The quicker-witted ladies present looked at Amy with interest (particularly Miss Enstone), and most of the gentlemen smiled fatuously upon Mr Jones, who had, they obviously thought, been very clever. Colonel Long, however, sighed and said with feeling, 'Your first, God bless him! My own dear lady is expecting our sixth. That's why she is unable to join us this evening. They're all very welcome, of course, but it seems that the house is permanently occupied by monthly nurses and the garden by wet napkins!'

'And may we soon hope to hear of Lord Stanford?' Miss Enstone enquired, her little sharp nose positively a-quiver. There was a moment of confused silence as her audience tried to work out whom she might mean, but naturally enough, it was Lord Cressing who replied, 'How clever of you to know what my son's title will be. No news as yet, but we live in hopes!'

'And did you enjoy your stay in Bath, Lady Cressing?' Miss Enstone pursued the matter indirectly.

'Oh, do pray call me Lucinda, as you always have!' that lady replied. 'It was very pleasant to see such a fine city, but the water wasn't much to my taste, and I'm glad to be home again.'

'What is wrong with the water?' asked Julia, being apparently unaware that Bath was a spa, although Caroline knew that she had been there with her godmother.

'It tastes of warm flat-irons,' Lucinda informed her. 'Though I'm sure it must be quite good for one, as unpleasant-tasting things usually are!'

'Ah, but so are good-tasting things,' her father observed, 'so may I tempt anyone to a little more of this mutton, or perhaps a morsel of roast duck?'

Fred, among others, admitted an interest, and was served along with everyone else, to Caroline's amusement, for the ginger resident in her own home took his meals alone in the back kitchen.

'Have you met many people in Woodham yet, Miss Barnes?' Mr Jones enquired of her as conversation became more general. 'I suppose not, as you arrived only on Friday.'

'I made the acquaintance of several people after church yesterday,' she replied. 'Oh, and I've encountered a gentleman—quite informally, I'm afraid—a Mr Bell. Perhaps you know him?'

'Bell?' Mr Jones looked puzzled. 'No, I don't think . . . Rector, do you know a Mr Bell in these parts?'

'There's a storekeeper at the powder-mill . . . but you said a gentleman?' Mr Calvert had obviously overheard Caroline.

'Yes. I'm afraid he introduced himself, but quite politely,' Caroline replied, wishing she had not mentioned the stranger as everyone had stopped talking to listen. 'He seems to know people in the town. He passed Mr Hartwell's chaise along the road as we were coming here, and bowed, and then I ran into him in the market on Saturday, and he spoke to me. He said his name is Bramwell Bell.'

Everyone looked at Miss Enstone, but she only frowned and shook her head, as puzzled as anyone.

'He's tall—as tall as Major Bridges, but more heavily built, and has fair, wavy hair. He rides a black horse.'

'Oh, I believe I've seen him when I was riding along the Forest edge!' Major Bridges exclaimed, 'but I don't know him.'

'I collect that the house on Claypit Hill in the Forest is let to a gentleman,' Miss Enstone said smugly. 'Admiral Hall's house, you know. I heard that the gentleman has been ill and is recuperating in the country air, but doesn't wish to go into company until he is better. That will be the gentleman, I'm sure!'

Having presumably identified the mysterious stranger, everyone but Caroline forgot about him and talked of other things, particularly as the next course was brought in and they were all busy offering or accepting helpings of the various dishes and congratulating Mrs Calvert on the excellence of her cook.

After dinner, the gentlemen were not long in joining the ladies in the parlour, although Fred did not put in an appearance, having an assignation elsewhere, and before long, Lucinda was persuaded to sing, and Amy Jones played a few pieces on the pianoforte. Then Caroline was asked if she would favour the company with a tune, which she was happy to do, after the usual polite protests of not having brought her music and not being up to Mrs Jones' standard, which she soon proved was not altogether true, as she had always practised diligently and was quite a good performer.

When it came to Julia's turn, she blushed and replied in a low and genuinely embarrassed voice that she was not able to contribute anything. 'I fear I've failed lamentably to keep in practice!' she admitted, 'But I promise I'll try to do better, and perhaps next time I'll manage a piece.'

Caroline noted with pleasure that she actually seemed to mean what she said, and, moreover, appeared to be enjoying the evening, especially, perhaps, as Major Bridges seemed to find her an object of some interest, which made Caroline wonder if perhaps the combination of a red coat and the looks of a dark-haired Apollo was beginning to eclipse the remembered attractions of 'dearest Charles'.

'I believe your cousin is quite impressed with the gallant Major,' Lord Cressing murmured to Caroline, with whom he happened to be sharing a sofa. 'Which is not unusual! But, what is less common, he's giving her all his attention instead of dividing it impartially among all the females present. They'd made a good couple, don't you think?'

'Perhaps, but would Mr Hartwell approve?' Caroline asked doubtfully.

Lord Cressing gave her an amused look and replied, 'You take your chaperonage seriously, then? Yes, I don't think you need have any fears on that score—he's quite impeccably eligible!' which Caroline was relieved to hear.

Her half-formulated hope that Julia's broken heart was about to be mended was dashed, however, on the way home, when she, in the darkness of the carriage, remarked mournfully, 'Oh, how every dark, handsome man reminds me of my dearest Charles! Alas, Cousin Caro, how can I survive?'

'Troubles do pass, my dear,' Caroline replied, feeling helpless. 'And you are very young.'

'I'm old enough to know my own feelings!' Julia protested a trifle petulantly.

'If I may give you a word of advice,' Caroline ventured cautiously, 'I would say that your brother seems to me to be the kind of man who would be the more determined the more he is opposed. Is it really wise to quarrel with him so much? In your father's absence, he has control over you, after all.'

As Julia's only reply to this sounded very much like an unladylike sniff, Caroline tried a slightly different tack, and continued, 'In any case, you will only make yourself ill if you mope about all the time, Cousin. Would it not be more sensible to try to occupy yourself and preserve your health so that, whatever may happen, you will be better prepared for it? The society here seems pleasant, and it will help you to—to bear your troubles better if you are distracted from them more, don't you think? After all, I believe you quite enjoyed yourself this evening?'

'Enjoyed!' Julia exclaimed. 'How can I enjoy myself when I am desolate? Well—perhaps I was a little diverted . . . Yes, I'll admit that it wasn't as unpleasant as I expected. In fact, I found the company not altogether

displeasing. What a busybody is that Miss Enstone! Did
you see how her little nose twitched with anticipation at every item of gossip? Quite like a mouse
scenting cheese, I do declare!' She gave a little gurgle of
laughter, which Caroline, who had already seen Miss
Enstone's resemblance to a mouse, could not help but
echo.

'Oh, but tell me, Cousin Caro. Your mysterious
admirer! When did you see him in the market? Was it
while I was buying my ribbon? Oh, what a shame! I
should love to have seen him! Is he handsome? Fair, you
said? But a fair man cannot be so handsome as a dark
one. Why could he not be dark?'

'As dark as Major Bridges?' Caroline asked slyly.

'Major Bridges? Yes, I suppose he is quite handsome
. . . he puts me in mind a little of my dearest Charles, but
only a little, mind! Ah, dear! What a strain it is to go into
company. I declare, I'm quite exhausted!'

Her exhaustion continued throughout the next day, so
Caroline, after failing to persuade her to take a walk,
made the best of it and went out herself with her
sketchbook and pencils, and climbed the hill to the lone
poplar, where she sat on the grass in its shade and
tried to sketch the view across the wide valley towards
the town. After half an hour or so, she held her
work at arm's length and compared it with the original,
feeling not entirely displeased with what she had
done.

'A very creditable picture!' said a pleasant voice
behind her. 'Although I believe you have made the
church tower a little too wide and squat.'

Caroline started and turned her head, to discover that
Mr Bell was leaning against the tree, the reins of his fine
black horse looped over his arm.

'I'm sorry—did I startle you?' he asked, smiling down
at her. 'You were so absorbed that I think you didn't

hear me come. I see you're alone—was Miss Hartwell not able to accompany you?'

'She was a little fatigued,' Caroline replied, feeling at a disadvantage, sitting on the grass and twisting round to look up at so tall a figure, but he took a few steps forward, and sat down nearby on the grass.

'I think perhaps that young lady isn't fond of walking in the country, for I've not seen her about in the fields,' he observed, not exactly in the form of a question.'

Caroline smiled ruefully, and admitted that Miss Hartwell was not overfond of walking.

'And Mr Hartwell, presumably, is away on one of his mysterious journeys?' Mr Bell continued, surveying the view with interest. It certainly was a fine prospect, with the various colours of the fields bright in the sunshine, the picturesque red roofs of the little town clustering round the white tower of the church, and the several streams of the river glittering like silver ribbons.

'You seem to know a great deal about us!' Caroline exclaimed, wondering uneasily what her mother would say about her entering into conversation with a stranger in this isolated spot.

'Oh, I've nothing better to do than idle away my time in listening to odd items of gossip!'

'I collect that you are convalescent from an illness,' Caroline said tentatively, wondering if he was indeed the man Miss Enstone had mentioned.

'There, you see! You know as much about me as I do about you!' he exclaimed. 'It's easy to deduce that, as Hartwell has brought you here to keep Miss Hartwell company, he is gone away himself. Tell me, now—am I right in thinking that your father is Josiah Barnes, the East India merchant?'

'Why, yes! Do you know him?'

'I believe I've met him a few times, in the way of business, and socially, too, for that matter, but I can really claim to know him well only by reputation. He's said to be a shrewd but honest man.'

Caroline took this as a compliment to her father, and quite warmed to Mr Bell, who was certainly most pleasant and well mannered, if a little unconventional in making himself known to a young lady without benefit of an introduction.

'I do hope you're finding your stay with your young cousin congenial,' he continued. 'I have heard, by rumour only (and rumour is a lying jade), that Miss Hartwell is a little temperamental, and not entirely happy at being brought into the country when she thought to be enjoying herself in Society!'

Caroline was not sure how to reply to this, and made a few more additions to her sketch while she considered the matter. 'She is a little disappointed,' she admitted eventually.

'Ah, well—I expect Mr Hartwell will make haste with his business and return as soon as may be. Perhaps he intends to be away only a few days?'

'I believe so,' Caroline replied, realising that, in fact, she had no idea, as Mr Hartwell had not said when he intended to return.

'Oh, pray don't add another line to your sketch!' Mr Bell exclaimed, for her pencil had become busy again of its own volition. 'It's quite perfect as it is. Do you mean to colour it?'

'I haven't brought my colouring-box out with me,' she replied, not having thought of it. 'But perhaps I shall return another day with it, for I don't think I would be able to capture the different shades from memory.'

'I hope that you will,' he said, smiling most charmingly at her, 'and quite soon, before the weather breaks, I shall look for you when I'm riding this way, and hope to see a finished picture before long.'

Caroline was flattered that he should think so well of her sketch, for she was much out of practice in her drawing, and thought herself that it had turned out better than she expected. She returned his smile, and was struck by the warmth of expression in his dark eyes, though some tiny part of her mind registered a fleeting impression of surprise that a man with such fair hair should have eyes that were almost black.

'I think I should be returning home,' she said, for the church clock had just struck four faintly across the fields. 'Miss Hartwell will wonder what is become of me!'

'Perhaps she'll think you're off with the raggle-taggle gipsies!'

Caroline laughed as she rose to her feet with as much grace as she could manage, encumbered with sketch-book and pencil-case. Mr Bell rose too, in one fluid movement, and held out a hand as if to assist her, but she thought it best not to notice.

'I, too, must be on my way,' he said. 'Doctor's orders, you know! You can find your way home from here?'

'Oh, yes—straight down the hill.'

'Then I'll wish you good afternoon, and thank you for a most enjoyable encounter.'

Caroline bade him goodbye, and set off down the slope towards Canons Grange. She glanced back once, and saw that Mr Bell was sitting his horse, watching her. He raised his hat and waved it, and, after a momentary hesitation, she lifted a hand in reply before going on her way, still in two minds about whether or not she should have entered into conversation with him at all.

'Oh, well, why not?' she concluded at last as she crossed the stableyard. 'He seems a pleasant enough gentleman, and no doubt he's lonely and glad of someone to pass the time of day with, being kept from going into company. I wonder what illness he has been

suffering? I hope it may not be a consumption, but I think
not, for he looks quite well. A little sallow, but not
pale or wasted away!'

CHAPTER
SIX

ON HER return to the house, Caroline went to her room to tidy herself, and then to the parlour, with a slight feeling of apprehension, to discover in what sort of a mood Julia might be found, but Miss Hartwell was, in fact, entertaining Major Bridges and Captain Marsh in a most vivacious fashion over the teacups.

Both military gentlemen sprang to their feet as Caroline entered, and Horatio rose from his customary torpor to investigate her, then appointed himself her guardian and insisted on lying at her feet, growling softly whenever either of the gentlemen handed her a cup and dish or a plate of sandwiches.

'That dog is quite demented!' Julia exclaimed. 'I declare, he lives in a state of total confusion! You see, he approached Miss Barnes as though she were a burglar, and now he fawns on her as though she is his dearest friend, all in the space of a minute! He's just the same with my brother, but ignores me completely! I dare say that if we had a real burglar, he would either welcome him with open paws, or take no notice of him at all!'

'Animals are often eccentric,' Major Bridges observed, smiling upon her in what, in a less godlike being, might have been thought a fatuous manner. 'Heaven only knows what clouds of unreasoning fill their minds! I had a charger once which would always bite one particular groom, although the man had never done him any harm!'

'Perhaps he liked the flavour,' Captain Marsh contributed, but, as he had a somewhat expressionless face, no one was sure whether he was joking or serious, and the remark met with no response.

'Have you had a pleasant walk, Cousin Caro?' Julia enquired brightly. 'Miss Barnes is greatly fond of fresh air and healthy exercise,' she added for the gentlemen's benefit, without waiting for Caroline's reply. 'I fear for her complexion, however, in this bright sunshine.'

'I hope you don't stay indoors for the sake of your own, for I'm sure that even a tropical sun could not mar such perfection!' Major Bridges replied gallantly. Caroline gave him a sharp glance, thinking that he was being a little fulsome, but the admiration on his face as he gazed at Julia appeared unfeigned, and she herself was certainly in looks, her habitual sulky expression quite gone, her eyes sparkling, and even her hair seeming to curl more crisply than usual. Caroline's hopes revived a little.

'I collect that you live in Town, Miss Barnes?' Captain Marsh enquired. 'You don't usually spend the summer in the country?'

'We live in Stepney, which was a village when my father first had our house built,' Caroline replied, 'but it's fast growing and joining up with the other villages, and with the City, and I think there will soon be no fields left. My mother talks of removing, perhaps to Paddington, or south of the river.'

'And have you lived all your life in Stepney?'

'Oh, no! I was born in the City, but my father thought best, with a growing family of children, to go more into the country, and we went to Stepney when I was five.'

'I believe my name appears in the registers of your parish church,' Captain Marsh said. 'Although I have never, I'm sure, so much as passed through the parish! What do you say to that, Miss Barnes?'

'But that's impossible!' Julia exclaimed. 'If your name is in the register, you must have been baptised there, surely?'

Caroline laughed, and said, 'Why, not necessarily! I collect that Captain Marsh was born at sea.'

'Indeed—in an East Indiaman, somewhere off the coast of Portugal, and baptised by a clerical fellow-passenger,' the Captain confirmed. 'I see that you know the peculiarity of your own church, Miss Barnes!' He added, for the benefit of the others, 'All baptisms at sea in British ships are registered at St Dunstan's, Stepney.'

Before they left, the officers persuaded Julia that she might well enjoy a walk in the Forest in their company, and she agreed, with Caroline's encouragement, that the officers should call on the next afternoon, if the weather continued fine, and ride on horseback to the Forest edge, accompanying herself and Caroline in the carriage, and then they would all stroll among the trees for a while.

'And we shall take Horatio,' she declared. 'It will do him good to run about and chase squirrels!'

In the event, the decision to take the dog proved an error, for as soon as he was released from the carriage, Horatio disappeared into the undergrowth, and the next hour was spent in a vain search for him. Eventually, Julia declared that Horatio might find his own way home as best he could, but she was not going to waste any more time on him, and, as the officers were not unwilling to abandon the pursuit, they all set out on their walk along the mossy paths amid fine beeches and hornbeams whose leaves were just beginning to turn, and graceful birches overhanging patches of bright heather. It was some time before they noticed that a bright-eyed dog was pacing sedately at heel just behind Caroline, and, by mutual unspoken consent, they all ignored him, lest notice should inspire him to run off again.

It was very pleasant in the Forest, with only the gentle sounds of the breeze in the tree-tops, the hum of bees in the heather, and the rustle of unseen animals in the browning bracken. Once, they emerged into a glade where a deer stood momentarily in a shaft of sunlight before bounding away among the trees, and occasionally they caught sight of the red-brown squirrels chasing up tree-trunks and along branches, absorbed in some game of their own. Once or twice Caroline thought she caught a glimpse, out of the corner of her eye, of something moving in the trees on a parallel course to the path they were taking, but whenever she turned her head in that direction, there was nothing there, so she concluded that it was some trick of the light on the trunks.

By the time they returned home, Julia had seen the humorous side of Horatio's conduct, admitted to having enjoyed her afternoon quite well, and was cheerful and complacent all the evening, so that Caroline, who had been wondering ever since Mr Hartwell mentioned the matter, if she should ask Julia if she had really tried to elope, was tempted to question her while she was in such a good humour. But, on reflection, she decided that to do so would probably only put her back into her martyred state and spoil the pleasure of the day.

She did, however, wish to know if Julia really had attempted such a desperate measure, and what had driven her to it, and she was considering how best to find out the next morning as, having risen and dressed, she looked out of her window to see what sort of a morning it might be, and was surprised to see Mr Hartwell walking down the garden in the early sunshine. Without stopping to think, and feeling a quite unreasonable lift to her spirits, she seized a shawl and fairly ran from the room, down the stairs, and out into the garden.

She came upon Mr Hartwell as he was putting a rose which he had just plucked into his buttonhole, and he looked up, his face breaking into a smile of surprise and what looked like pleasure.

'Why, Cousin Caroline! Good morning!' he exclaimed, took two strides towards her, put his hands on her shoulders, and kissed her warmly on the cheek.

It was totally unexpected, and so was her own re-action, for she found herself having difficulty in taking a breath, and a most peculiar quivering feeling ran through her as she started back and pulled away from his hands.

'Mr Hartwell!' she exclaimed breathlessly.

He gave a wry smile, and said, 'Am I never to be promoted to the glory of Cousin Robert, then?'

'But you are not my cousin,' she said flatly.

'True, but is there not sufficient connection for an honorary cousinship? Or perhaps just plain Robert?' There was a quizzical look on his face, and an odd watchfulness in his eyes, and she decided that he was teasing her.

'I wish to ask you something,' she said resolutely, ignoring his question, which she was reluctant to answer in her present confusion.

'Yes?'

'You said that Julia tried to elope—was it true?'

'Of course, else I should not have said so.'

'Oh!'

'Have you not asked her?'

'I hardly like to,' Caroline replied uncertainly, not sure how to go on. 'It was such a dreadful thing, and if she did not, she would be so—so . . .'

'Insulted?' he offered.'

'Yes. I think she would be most offended, and not wish to be friendly with me . . .'

'And then you could go home with a clear consience,' he said matter-of-factly.

'I should not like my visit to end in that way. You're quite right in saying that she needs someone of her own sex and age to keep her company, and she is very unhappy.'

Mr Hartwell turned away for a moment to cut another rose, which he silently handed to Caroline. She took it almost absent-mindedly and threaded its stem through the trimming on her morning-frock while she considered how to proceed.

'I think,' she said at length, 'that I should like to know something more of the circumstances before I decide whether to mention it to her.'

'Very well.' Mr Hartwell gestured towards a wooden bench which was set at an angle of the path and commanded a good view across the garden. 'Then let us sit here, and I'll tell you.'

He produced a handkerchief from his sleeve and brushed away any drops of dew which might have remained on the bench. Caroline sat down at one end, and he at the other, half-turned towards her.

'As you know, Julia had been living with her godmother since her parents went abroad. Lady Staveley decided, against my wishes, to bring her Out last year, and she has been mixing in Society—some of it not altogether what I would have approved, had I known. She met Sir Charles Corbin, became enamoured of him, and, apparently realising that I wouldn't encourage the connection, took some care that I shouldn't hear of it!' He glanced briefly at Caroline.

'I will admit that, through pressure of affairs, I've not seen as much of Julia in the past year as I should have done, but I assumed, having heard nothing to the contrary, that she was safe and happy with Lady Staveley, and I was very busy . . . However, a few weeks ago, I knew that they were in Brighton, and my business took me into Sussex, so I decided to make a detour and visit them, to see how Julia did. Through various problems, it was near to midnight as I approached Brighton, and, in a narrow lane on a tight bend, my chaise locked wheels with a phaeton travelling rather too fast in the opposite direction! Of course, I got down to see what damage had been done, and so did the two people in the phaeton . . . Imagine my surprise to find that they were Corbin and my sister, who had enough valises and hatboxes with her to equip an army!'

'Oh, dear!' Caroline exclaimed, her eyes very wide and shocked in her serious face. 'How dreadful! What did you do?'

'I enquired where they thought they were going at that time of night, to which Julia made no reply except to burst into tears, and Corbin said, "Gretna Green—that is, provided . . ." No! I'll not tell you what else! Suffice to say that I lost my temper and drew his cork!'

'You hit him?' Caroline exclaimed, horrified.

'Knocked him down—and out, I believe, although he was a good stone the heavier.' Mr Hartwell's voice contained just a suspicion of pleasure at the recollection. 'Meanwhile, the grooms had sorted out the tangled wheels and mine had no damage, so I pushed Julia into the chaise, flung her belongings in after her, and suffered her hysterics all the way to Brighton, where I had Lady Staveley roused, and we had something of a disagreement—she had hysterics too!' he added grimly. 'It was not a pleasant experience! I brought Julia away with me, of course.'

Caroline was silent for a few moments, considering what she had been told, and then she ventured, trying to be tactful, 'I suppose you consider Julia too young to be married?'

'That has nothing to say to the matter!' he replied flatly. 'Did you enjoy eating your mutton at the Rectory?'

'Yes, very much, and I believe Julia did too, though she would not admit to it.'

'Major Bridges was there, too, no doubt.' It was a statement, not a question.

'Yes.' Caroline bit her lip, then added, 'Lord Cressing mentioned to me that the Major is—er—"impeccably eligible", I believe were his exact words.'

'I'm grateful for your consideration in enquiring. Had you any particular reason to do so?'

'It was just an idea I had, but I shall probably prove to be wrong . . . On the other hand, he and Captain Marsh called the next day and were made welcome, and yesterday we walked with the two officers in the Forest.'

'Walked!' Mr Hartwell's eyebrows rose. 'And was it enjoyable?'

'Very, apart from a little difficulty with Horatio.'

'I collect that the redoubtable canine accompanied you. I suppose he ran off.'

'Yes, but he returned of his own accord, once we had stopped looking for him, and walked with me very properly afterwards.'

'My felicitations! He must have taken a great liking for you—he never walks properly with anyone, apart from his own particular footman, and then only on a leash. I believe it may be time for breakfast—shall we go in?'

Caroline assented, although there was still a question which she wished to ask him, but she thought there would be time for it on the way back to the house. However, as they walked along the path, Mr Hartwell lightly placed a hand on her elbow, as if to steady her ascent of the occasional step which broke the line of their walk, and she experienced the same strange internal quivering sensation which had surprised her before, and it quite put the carefully assembled wording of her question out of her head, and so it remained unasked.

Julia's demeanour at breakfast was back to her old, disagreeable, quarrelsome manner, and was, if anything, worse than it had been before her brother's absence. She even greeted him with a sharp, 'Oh, so you're back to spoil everything!', to which he riposted equably, 'But surely it's your expression which has soured the milk?' Caroline felt that this was hardly a helpful reply, but its effect on Julia was, perhaps, desirable, as she retreated into silence and they were at least spared her usual attempts to pick a quarrel with her brother during the meal.

As Mr Hartwell did not seem particularly desirous of conversation either, Caroline gave up trying and followed her own line of thought instead, going over her recent talk with him, and, recalling the last part, began to feel that there had been a note of mockery in his voice directed at herself, which only served to confirm her conviction that he was an odiously arrogant man. And yet . . . Uneasily, she realised that she had actually felt pleased when she looked out of the window and saw him in the garden. How very odd!

'What do you think, Cousin Caroline?' His voice broke into her thoughts, startling her, for she had been so absorbed in considering the peculiarity of being pleased to see such a disagreeable person that she had not heard him speak before.

'I'm sorry?' she said, turning towards him and meeting his eyes, which studied her face thoughtfully, and, to her mortification, she felt her cheeks redden. 'Did you say something?'

'I wondered aloud if it might be considered another example of my perfidy if I invited a few of the younger people to dinner,' he replied. 'Of course, if it would be likely to cause anyone to fly into the boughs and disrupt the harmony of this contented household I should say no more. What do you think?'

'Why ask her?' Julia demanded sullenly. 'I know perfectly well that this is some plot of yours to try to make me forget dearest Charles, and it won't wash! I saw you with your heads together in the garden this morning, working it all out.'

'Well, if Cousin Julia believes that, I should strongly advise against asking anyone to dine here,' Caroline said at once. 'Of course, if she thinks it may be a conspiracy, she would quite rightly consider herself free to be as rude to your guests as she pleased. Perhaps it might be better . . . But it's not my place to advise you, for I am, after all, but a guest in your house . . .'

'Pray, advise!' Mr Hartwell replied calmly, pouring himself another cup of coffee.

'I was only about to say that perhaps Cousin Julia might like to give a little dinner-party herself,' Caroline ventured. 'I'm not sure if that would be *de règle*? I suppose it would be, though, as she's Out . . .'

'Yes,' said Julia firmly. 'I shall give a dinner-party. You need not attend, Robert!'

'Thank you. Perhaps you will think to tell me when it will be, so that I may find myself a corner somewhere to dine on the scraps from your table?' Mr Hartwell said drily. 'Or maybe I can appeal to the Rector's charity . . .'

'The Rector and Mrs Calvert will be dining with me,' Julia pronounced. 'You may come if you wish, provided you do not interfere.'

Mr Hartwell had been drinking his coffee as she spoke. He choked slightly at her last sentence, and said, 'Thankee!' briefly when he had recovered.

'In fact,' Julia continued, looking remarkably smug, 'you may partner Miss Enstone.'

'I had hoped you might allow me the solace of Cousin Caroline,' Mr Hartwell replied with a poignant sigh and an enigmatic look in her direction. 'May I at least beg you will not fix on Saturday week for your entertainment?'

'Why?'

'Because I've already arranged to hold the Harvest Supper then for the estate workers.'

'A Harvest Supper! Oh, how delightful!' Caroline exclaimed before Julia could think of the blighting reply which she was obviously formulating. 'My mother has often told of the harvest feasts she remembered from her girlhood. She lived in the country then, you know.'

'Then, pray, consider yourself invited to mine,' Mr Hartwell said at once. 'Julia, of course, will be expected in any case.'

'Oh? By whom?' the young lady enquired in a dangerous tone.

'By all the people, of course! Every year you've been away, they've drunk your health and wished you had been with them. They'll be delighted to have one daughter of the house there at last! If only we might have both.' He added the last in an oddly subdued voice, contrasting with the hearty tone—falsely hearty, in Caroline's ears —of the rest of the speech.

'Oh!' Julia had clearly had the wind taken out of her sails. 'Well, if I'm to have a dinner-party and a Harvest Supper, I shall have to set Susan and the sewing-woman to work on two new gowns, for I declare I haven't a rag fit to be seen! Of course, it would be easier to go to Town and buy something . . .'

'Forty miles for a couple of gowns? That's a trifle beyond reason!' Mr Hartwell said scornfully. 'Besides, the off-side wheeler's lame, and I want her fit for Monday, for I've to go into Kent.'

'Kent?' Julia said musingly. 'What could take you into Kent? There's nothing there!'

Mr Hartwell raised his eyes to heaven. 'Nothing in Kent!' he murmured. 'A naval dockyard, a gunpowder-mill, hopfields, cherry orchards, a few thousand people, the Archbishop of Canterbury and the Lord Warden of the Cinque Ports—all dismissed as nothing! Buy some silk from the mill in West Street, and charge it to me, if you must have new gowns. Only two pieces, mind! I'll not go to the Marshalsea for your wardrobe.'

'If you insist, dear Robert!' Julia sweetly, looking as if she might purr if someone stroked her. 'Cousin Caro and I will go there directly and see what they have. You'd like that, wouldn't you, Cousin Caro?'

'A walk across the fields before luncheon would be very pleasant,' Caroline replied, which made Julia pout, but she caught Caroline's eye, and reluctantly agreed to go on foot to the mill, perhaps seeing that she really did prefer to walk.

They set off quite soon after breakfast, and took a different route from that by which they had returned from the market, crossing over the Cornmill stream by a pretty little iron bridge within the Canons Grange lands, and then striking out across a wide pasture towards a group of buildings some distance further west.

'Is that the silk-mill?' Caroline asked, glancing nervously over her shoulder at a herd of cows standing about in the pasture.

'No, that's the powder-mill,' Julia replied, flourishing her parasol. 'The army camp's just up there, to the north, and the powder-mill extends from it almost to West Street, just beyond the end of the town. There's a stream flows through the powder-mill, and another comes off it and goes along this side, then under West Street just at the town's end, and works the silk-mill.'

The line of the silk-mill stream was marked by trees planted at intervals along the bank, some willow, but most of another variety which Caroline could not identify, but which she later found out were alders. These had not been pollarded, but spread their branches in a screen along the bank, and also across the water, meeting above it and forming a tunnel over the swiftly-flowing stream. Their roots made walking along the path an operation requiring some attention if one was not to trip over, and conversation languished as a result, but presently Julia, who was leading the way, stopped and turned round to speak.

'What were you and Robert discussing in the garden this morning?' she demanded.

Caroline curbed her natural irritation at this peremptory question, remembering that Julia had good reason to suspect her half-brother of interfering in her affairs behind her back, and replied in as calm a tone as she could, 'Oh, I asked what he meant by saying that you tried to elope, that's all.'

'All! He accuses me of . . . Well, that beats all!' Julia exclaimed indignantly. 'Just because dearest Charles took me for a drive, and we were a little late returning. It was not our fault that an accident delayed us. Oh, please, dear Cousin Caro, don't let him set you against me! I should hate to be bad friends with you, truly I would!' She gazed at her with tear-filled eyes.

'Of course I shall not turn against you!' Caroline replied reassuringly, wondering why Mr Hartwell should have presented such a black picture of an escapade which, in Julia's version, sounded fairly harmless, if a little indiscreet, for a young lady should not go driving alone with a gentleman, particularly in a phaeton. 'But why . . . ?'

She had meant to ask why Julia had luggage with her if she were not eloping, but a third voice joined the conversation at that point, in a shrill, panic-stricken treble from a short distance further down the stream.

''Elp!' it said. 'Please, 'elp!'

The ladies looked about them, bewildered, for there was no sign of anyone, but the sound of splashing drew their attention to the stream. Caroline pushed through the branches until she could see the water, and there, a dozen yards or so downstream, an agonised face peered at her over a low-hanging branch.

'There's someone in the river!' she exclaimed, scrambling to get out again from the mesh of branches, and tearing her frock in the process.

'Where?' asked Julia, who could not even see the water from the path.

Caroline was already hastening along the path to a spot as near as she could judge to where she had seen the head, and there found a gap between the trees, and a boy of eight or nine, right in the middle of the stream, clinging desperately to the low branch. Although his frightened eyes were fixed on Caroline, he continued to cry ''Elp! 'Elp!' in a hoarse croak, as though he had been shouting for so long that his voice had almost gone.

'Just be quiet and hold on!' Caroline commanded. 'We'll have you out in a minute!' She surveyed the situation calmly and quickly. The water did not look particularly deep, but would probably be over the boy's head if he tried to stand on the bottom, and the current was strong, pulling on his body, and he looked as if he could not hold on much longer. He had stopped croaking, but was now sobbing convulsively.

'Oh, dear! We must run for help!' Julia exclaimed, peering over Caroline's shoulder.

'I doubt there's time for that!' Caroline was untying her bonnet-strings and hanging her bonnet, reticule and gloves on a convenient twig. Her pelisse came off next, and then her boots.

'What are you going to do?' Julia asked, wringing her hands in a singularly ineffective fashion.

'Wade in and get him, of course. Hold on to my hand while I climb down the bank.'

Julia took her hand, but was too busy exclaiming and protesting to be much help to Caroline as she slid down the bank and into the water, which was very cold and reached almost to her armpits.

'Oh, do be careful!' Julia cried, letting go of Caroline's hand in order to wring both her own again.

'Listen!' Caroline said. 'I think I hear hoofbeats. See if anyone is coming, and call for help if there is!'

As Julia turned away to run out into the field, screeching 'Help! Help!' in a very shrill voice, Caroline braced herself and began to wade out into the stream, holding on to the branch to which the child was clinging, and trying each foothold before she put any weight on it.

'What's your name?' she asked conversationally, to keep his mind off the precariousness of his position.

'What you want to know for? I ain't done nothing!'

'Well, you've fallen in the river,' she pointed out. 'My name is Caroline Barnes. Won't you tell me yours?'

'You'll get me into trouble!' the boy replied. 'I'll get sent to Orstrily or to sea in the Fleet, and my dad'll beat me!'

Caroline deduced from this that the boy had been breaking the law in some way when he met with his present misfortune, so she gave up questioning him, and concentrated on reaching him. It was not as easy as she had expected, for the current was strong and tugged at her skirts, pulling her off-balance, and those same skirts tended to catch her legs and trip her. To make it even more difficult, the bed of the stream was littered with loose stones, and there were holes in places. She stepped into one which was deep enough to plunge her up to her chin before she could get out of it. It seemed an age before she could stretch out and take a firm grip of the boy's clothing.

'Now, start to pull yourself along the branch towards me,' she ordered.

'Can't,' he replied, sobbing. 'Me arms is pulled near out of the sockets. I can't move!'

'Yes, you can! You have to, for we can't stay here all day!' she said sharply. 'Now I'm going to pull you, so move your hands along the branch, one by one.'

She gave a sharp tug at the boy's shirt, pulling him towards her, and he made a series of frantic little grabs at the branch, eventually coming close enough for her to get her hands under his arms. She then had to persuade him to let go of the branch so that she could tow him back to the bank, walking backwards herself and feeling at every step for a safe foothold. She was so startled when a firm pair of hands seized her by the shoulders that she almost let go of the boy, but Mr Hartwell's voice said in her ear, 'That's the ticket! Turn a little upstream, if you can, so that I can pull him out.'

Between them, they heaved the boy out on to the bank, where he scrambled to his feet, said, 'Thankee very kindly, missus! Thankee, sir!', and then took to his heels and ran as fast as his wobbly legs would carry him towards the town, nearly knocking Julia over as he went.

'Well, of all the ingratitude!' she exclaimed indignantly.

'He did say his thank-yous quite prettily,' Mr Hartwell pointed out. 'Now, Caroline, put your arms about my neck, and I'll contrive to get you out.'

'But your coat will be soaked!' she protested, feeling more agitated by the thought of putting her arms about his neck than she had been by wading into the stream.

'I'll take it off first, then,' he replied, doing so, and failing to point out that it was already soaked from getting the boy out. 'Now, come along! You'll take a chill if you stand about in the water much longer.'

His method of getting her out was unorthodox but effective, and ended with them standing on the bank pressed closely together, Caroline's arms about his neck, and his about her waist, and, strangely, neither seemed in any great hurry to break apart.

'My gallant Caroline!' he murmured into her ear, and then something warm pressed against that same ear, giving Caroline the impression that he had kissed it, which seemed most unlikely.

'How are we to get Cousin Caro home?' Julia exclaimed agitatedly. 'I suppose we could hire a carriage at the Swan, but she can't walk through the streets like that!'

Which was true enough, for muslin has an unfortunate tendency to become transparent when wet!

CHAPTER
SEVEN

THE PROBLEM was easily solved. Mr Hartwell, having draped his coat about Caroline's shoulders over her re-donned pelisse, put her up on his horse and mounted behind her, promising to take her home as quickly as possible.

'What am I to do?' Julia demanded.

'Go and buy your silk,' Mr Hartwell replied indifferently. 'You said the purchase was urgent,' and he rode off before Julia could reply.

At first, he put the horse to a canter, but this was an uncomfortable gait for Caroline, sitting sideways, with nothing to hold on to but Mr Hartwell himself, which she was not anxious to do, for being so close to him was giving her a very peculiar feeling of breathlessness which she did not wish to aggravate. Presently, realising that she was being jounced about, he slowed his mount to a trot, and this made her position easier.

'How do you suppose he came to be in the river?' she asked. 'I gather it was something nefarious, for he wouldn't tell me his name.'

'Poaching fish, I expect! I think we should refrain from telling anyone about this little escapade, if you're agreeable. The fishing is preserved, and the owner not sympathetic to poachers, however young. The child could be transported, for it wouldn't be his first offence.'

'I'm quite agreeable, for I'd not wish to get him into any more trouble, although I couldn't, in any case, for I don't know his name!'

'I do,' Mr Hartwell replied drily. 'I've found him in my coverts often enough!'

'And prosecuted him?' Caroline wished her question had not sounded quite so much like an accusation.

'There were some articles recently in the *Edinburgh Review* . . .' Mr Hartwell apparently ignored the question. 'They were highly critical of the Game Laws, but in such a witty fashion . . . Perhaps you read them?'

'My father doesn't subscribe to it, as it's Whiggish,' Caroline replied a trifle primly. She was beginning to feel extremely cold and uncomfortable, and it was difficult not to shiver, which Mr Hartwell apparently noticed, for he suddenly exclaimed, 'This won't do! Passing our time in idle chatter when you're like to freeze! Hold tight!' He suited his own actions to his words, tightening his arms about her, and spurred his horse to a gallop, which, despite the double burden, the fine animal was able to keep up all the way to the house, with Caroline too busy clinging to Mr Hartwell in order not to fall off to be able to say anything more.

A hot bath and a brisk towelling soon put her to rights, and she firmly declined his suggestion that she should take to her bed and let the doctor be summoned. He did, however, persuade her to take a finger of brandy in her coffee, and by the time Julia returned, somewhat out of temper at having to walk home alone, she was quite restored and ready for her luncheon.

During the afternoon, Mr Hartwell went off somewhere unspecified, and Julia was torn between a need to rest after the exertions of the morning and a need, which proved to be the greater, to oversee the cutting-out of the new gowns to be made from her lengths of silk. So Caroline was able to slip away by herself, ostensibly to finish the sketch she had started of the view from the poplar tree, but actually intending to think about her position in the household and determine whether or no she should stay any longer.

She told herself, as she climbed the hill, that it was

quite ridiculous to be dithering in this fashion when she had already determined once that she should stay for Julia's sake, and it was not as if anything of any great moment had occurred to change her mind. After all, Mr Hartwell was still as arrogant as he had ever been, and she was not a green girl to be set in a flutter just because he had paid her a little attention—a very little, in fact . . . It was her own reaction to it which surprised her, for she had never been set into such a turmoil before by a mere touch or a look . . .

Mr Bell was sitting under the poplar when she reached it, his horse tethered to a nearby bush. He rose to his feet as she approached, bade her 'Good afternoon', then added, 'I'll not try to pretend that I came this way entirely without thinking that I might see you, but I hardly expected you'd be allowed out alone, as I believe the Lord and Master is returned!'

'Why should that prevent me from coming out?' Caroline enquired, making no comment on the rest of his speech.

'Rumour has it that he guards his womenfolk like the Sultan of Turkey and never lets his poor sister out of the house without an armed guard, so I assumed he would take the same attitude towards you, particularly in view of his expectations.'

'Expectations?' Caroline's curiosity was aroused sufficiently to make her pause in setting out her water-bottle, paints and brushes. 'What can you mean?'

'Well, I may be wronging the gentleman.' Mr Bell was eyeing her quizzically. 'For rumour, as I've remarked before, is a lying jade, but it is said that the high and mighty future Baron is short of the ready, and desperate enough to consider an alliance with Trade. Perhaps there's no truth in it . . . Have you seen any bailiffs lurking among the rose-bushes?'

'I'm not sure I should recognise one if I did,' Caroline

said lightly. 'Do they have green wings with red spots, or eleven legs?' The reply slipped out casually enough, but she was thinking at the same time that it would explain a great deal . . . The unexpected invitation, the feeling that Mr Hartwell was trying for some reason to please her. The idea gave her a curious sensation of flatness and disappointment.

'You ain't really going to paint the sky purple, are you?' he enquired in a lazy drawl.

Caroline looked at her picture with some surprise, and found that she was indeed holding a brush loaded with colour poised over the celestial region of it, and that colour was a particularly rich and pleasing purple.

'How provoking!' she exclaimed. 'Now, if I wanted purple, you may be sure that I'd never achieve quite such a good one!'

'That's due to the recalcitrance of inanimate objects,' Mr Bell assured her. 'Have you not noticed how any inanimate object always goes out of its way to be a awkward and disobliging as it can? Buttons drop off for no good reason, important letters mislay themselves, and stairs trip one up unprovoked. It's all part of a vast secret conspiracy of the inanimate against humanity!'

'Yes, of course—that explains it. I'm sure I had not thought of purple, or even red, when I began to paint!' Caroline exclaimed, diverted by the plausibility of the idea. 'Do you suppose they all work together, and decide beforehand which button shall come off next, or whether one's shawl shall snag on a bush or a nail? Is it truly a vast conspiracy? Should there not be a Parliamentary Committee set up to deal with it?'

'With our present government, that would simply be adding another inanimate object to the plot!' he replied sardonically. 'Best leave Parliament to play with trivial matters, like Bonaparte, and we more intelligent beings will contrive to fight the Great International Menace of the Inanimate on Behalf of all Mankind!'

Caroline smiled at him, thinking how amusing and easily companionable he was, compared with . . . with certain other persons, and really quite handsome, although there was something a little odd about his appearance which vaguely troubled her, but she could not pin down quite what it was . . . Something to do with the sallowness of his skin against that fair hair . . . She recalled that Miss Enstone had said he had been very ill, which would account, no doubt, for his looking sallow —something feverish, perhaps.

'You must think me very remiss,' she said. 'How are you? Are you making a good recovery?'

'From what?' he asked, frowning.

'Your illness.'

'Oh—yes, tolerably so, thank you. I must still lead a quiet life for some weeks, however, Plenty of fresh air and gentle exercise, but no excitement, and no going into company.'

'Am I tiring you with my chatter? You must say if it's too much for you.'

'Not at all!' The charming smile was back in evidence at once. 'A half-hour of conversation with you does me more good than a fortnight at Bath, or a year of sea-bathing. However, I believe that your hopeful suitor is coming in search of you, and I fear a meeting with him would give me a relapse! So, with your permission, I'll be on my way.'

He rose to his feet, and, with surprising speed, re-trieved his horse, made his farewell, and had already disappeared over the far side of the ridge before Mr Hartwell emerged from the Canons Grange garden and came up the hill towards Caroline.

'I wondered where you'd got to,' he said when he arrived. 'It's too bad of Julia to neglect you like this.'

'Not at all!' Caroline protested. 'I'm quite happy to sit

here, admiring the view and trying to capture it on paper. I'm not one to weary of my own company, I assure you!'

'I thought I saw someone with you . . .' Mr Hartwell looked about him in a puzzled fashion, for there was no sign of any living creature nearer than a hedger at work three fields away.

'Oh, that was Mr Bell. He stopped for a few words on his way by,' Caroline said airily, concentrating on her painting. 'He's the gentleman who's staying at some Admiral's house in the Forest, recovering from an illness.'

'You know him?'

'I've run into him a few times,' she replied vaguely, aware that her reply, although not untrue, would probably lead Mr Hartwell to think that Mr Bell had been introduced to her at some time in the City.

'Why don't you invite him to Julia's dinner-party, when she makes up her mind when it's to be?'

'He isn't permitted to go into Society, for he's been ill and has to be quiet and rest.'

'Talking of which'—he had already lost interest in Mr Bell—'should you not be resting yourself? Do you feel quite well after your adventure?'

'Why, I did nothing to endanger my well-being!' Caroline exclaimed. 'A few minutes in the water—no more than many people endure at the seaside for the benefit of their health!'

'I was afraid you might have taken a chill,' he said doubtfully. 'However—if you're sure you've taken no harm . . . I must say, your conduct was admirable! The poor child might well have drowned had you not gone to his rescue. I'm sure few females could have acted with such presence of mind and courage.'

Caroline experienced a most peculiar mixture of pleasure and chagrin—pleasure at being praised by a man who clearly had very high standards and was not given to paying compliments, and chagrin at his implied poor opinion of females in general. 'It hardly takes much presence of mind to do the obvious, and very little courage to do no more than get wet!' she replied a shade reprovingly. 'Any fool could have rescued the child—his only danger lay in his height being less than the depth of the water!'

'I noticed that Julia abstained from assisting, and only managed to screech and wring her hands,' he said in his most dry and sarcastic manner.

'There was no sense in both of us getting wet, and I asked her to call for help,' Caroline replied as snubbingly as she was able. 'I didn't know it was you, of course, or I'd have asked her to call you more melodiously!'

Mr Hartwell looked at her with something like astonishment, and then his expression softened into a smile, which warmed his dark eyes and gave his face a liveliness which was normally lacking. Caroline thought that he was really quite handsome when he allowed his face to emerge from behind his usual mask of hauteur—or guardedness. She suddenly realised that he quite often looked as if he might be deliberately hiding his feelings or his thoughts . . .

There was silence for a few minutes as she applied herself to her painting, trying to get the proper gradation of tone in the more distant fields. Mr Hartwell sat down, clasped his hands about his bent knees, and stared into the distance, then said abruptly, 'There's been a most disgraceful business in Portugal!'

Surprised by the anger in his voice, she looked up and said, 'How is that?'

'It appears that Wellesley, having trounced Junot at Vimiero, was superseded by a couple of idiots—Burrard and Dalrymple—whose only claim to importance was higher rank than his. They promptly concluded a convention with Junot which allowed his entire army to return to France, bag and baggage, all ready and equipped to fight us somewhere else—in Spain, probably. And, would you credit it!—they have been taken home in our ships, at our expense!'

'Why, that's iniquitous!' Caroline exclaimed, seeing the implications remarkably quickly. 'There was no point in Sir Arthur fighting them at all, in that case, and all the men who were killed in the battle . . .'

'Died for nothing!' Mr Hartwell finished for her. 'The whole business stinks of treason, to my view! They're to be recalled to face a board of enquiry—should be a court-martial, most people think. Good heavens! They shot Admiral Byng for less!'

'Sir Arthur must be furious!' Caroline said thoughtfully. She had heard tales of the force of Sir Arthur Wellesley's cold anger from her father's John Company friends who had known him in India.

'He must be beside himself! He's recalled as well!'

'As a witness?'

'No—as the third defendant. It seems perfectly obvious that he had nothing to do with it!'

'But what will happen to the army in Portugal, if all the generals are recalled?'

'Johnny Moore's out there. Presumably he'll take command, and there's Beresford, of course, with the Portuguese, but his British rank is very junior, for all that he's a Portuguese Marshal. You seem to have a good grasp of military affairs!'

'I can read a news-sheet!' Caroline replied tartly, aware of the unspoken 'for a female' at the end of his sentence. 'And my brothers and my father discuss the affairs of the world a great deal.'

'I'm beginning to think that you've taken a dislike to me,' he said abruptly. 'Have I committed some particular crime, or do you object to me in principle?'

Caroline hesitated, completely thrown by this facer, and was suddenly aware that, in spite of all the things she disliked *about* him, she did not actually dislike him, which was so paradoxical that she felt she would need two or three weeks alone on a desert island to sort it out!

'Why did you tell me that Julia tried to elope?' she asked in lieu of an answer.

'Because she did.'

'She says she did not.'

'Then one of us is a liar.'

'Oh.'

'The question is—which?'

She regarded him gravely, wondering, and he said coldly, 'I am not accustomed to having my word doubted. I have provided a rational and truthful account of my reasons for removing Julia from the care of her godmother, but apparently your taste for Gothic novels compels you to seek a darker and more devious explanation. I'm sorry. I have nothing more to say on the subject. Have you finished your picture? You have? Shall we descend in search of tea, then?'

'Yes, if you please,' Caroline replied equally coldly, fuming within as she emptied her water-bottle on a daisy which looked to be in need of encouragement, and packing up her paintbox. How dare he imply that she was allowing her imagination to run away with her! What right had he to assume that his word must be taken, even when he flatly contradicted his own sister! She suffered him to remove her painting equipment from her hands in order to carry it for her, but the few remarks which they exchanged on the way home were distinctly formal.

They found Julia in the parlour, quite exhausted from supervising the cutting of her silk and the subsequent pinning-up, and refreshing herself with china tea, with only Horatio for company. The latter made a cursory assault on his master's boots, more from habit than conviction, and then transferred his attention to Caroline with much tail-wagging and rolling about in a hopeful fashion, to which she responded by rubbing his stomach gently with her foot as she sat drinking her tea and listening to a detailed account of the cutting-out from Julia.

'Oh—by the way . . .' Julia interrupted herself to say off-handedly to her silent half-brother, who had taken refuge over by one of the windows with the cucumber sandwiches. 'I have sent out invitations for next Wednesday. You may come if you're back from wherever you said you were going.'

'Am I allowed to know anything of your guest-list?' he enquired.

'Why?'

'Well, if it sounds too crashingly boring, I could endeavour to be delayed in Kent—an urgent summons to visit the Archbishop, perhaps . . .'

'He's in residence at Lambeth,' Caroline put in solemnly, which caused Mr Hartwell to regard her less stonily.

'It's to be quite a small party.' Julia ignored the exchange. 'The Rector and Mrs Calvert, for I suppose I should return their hospitality, and Lord and Lady Cressing, and Captain Marsh to partner Cousin Caro, and Major Bridges, of course . . .'

'Of course,' Mr Hartwell echoed, with no particular expression.

'And, if you are returned, I shall ask Miss Enstone, but if not . . .'

'I shall return. How could I bear to miss an evening with Miss Enstone!'

Caroline unconsciously frowned at him, for she thought it unkind to make fun of a defenceless female of a certain age behind her back, but he caught the frown, interpreted it correctly, and added, 'I'm quite serious! I value Miss Enstone very highly. She's a kind lady who does much good among the poor, to the extent of going without herself all too often! She is also a valuable source of information on local affairs, and many a poor family has been put in the way of some help by a word in the right ear from Miss Enstone.'

Caroline felt, as she was probably intended to feel, set down, but it was not in her nature to remain miffed for more than a few minutes, and common sense told her that she had no reason to feel offended, for she had not actually said anything, and she had apparently mis-judged Mr Hartwell in her thoughts.

'What tempting dishes do you propose to set before us?' he asked Julia.

'I shall leave that to Cook,' she replied airily. 'There's no sense in keeping a dog'—Horatio gave an indignant rumble—'and barking oneself!'

'I thought you were about to say "*baking* oneself"!' Mr Hartwell rose to his feet and replaced his cup on the tea-tray. 'If you'll excuse me—I have to see the keeper about something or other feathered—I don't recall whether he said partridge, pheasant or peacock. Coming, Horatio?'

The dog sat up with ears pricked, looked at Master, made as if to go with him, then looked up at Caroline and subsided again.

'Traitor!' Mr Hartwell remarked bitterly, and went out.

'How odd!' Julia exclaimed. 'I've never known him decline to accompany Robert before. Perhaps his taste is improving!'

It was unfortunate that Mr Hartwell, having gone out, should have come back into the room in time to hear her last sentence, but he made no more response to it than a quirk of the eyebrows, and said, 'I forgot to mention that we are to have a visitor tomorrow.'

'A visitor!' Julia cried, all animation. 'Oh, is it dearest Godmother?'

'It most certainly is not!' Mr Hartwell replied icily. 'Cousin Caroline's mother has expressed her intention of calling on us tomorrow.'

'Mama?' Caroline was surprised, for the distance from Stepney to Woodham seemed overlong for a morning call. 'Oh dear! Is something amiss at home?' A rapid series of pictures of domestic horrors flitted through her mind, from Alice having the measles to Cook giving notice.

She was considerably relieved to hear Mr Hartwell reply calmly, 'I believe not. I understand that she wishes merely to set her mind at ease concerning your welfare. No doubt she suspects that I may have sold you into slavery, or confined you on bread and water in a damp cellar, but she said when the arrangement was made only that she wished to be sure that all was well with you. The visit was arranged when I called on her last Monday, on my way through London. I suggested that she come to luncheon, and stay the night, and she was pleased to agree.'

'Your mother!' Julia exclaimed as soon as she could get a word in. 'Oh, how delighted I shall be to meet dear Aunt Barnes! My own mother's sister! I shall go at once to consult with Cook about luncheon and dinner tomorrow, and to see which room would be best for her.'

'It's already seen to,' Mr Hartwell cut in before she could depart to cause havoc in the household. 'Carter has given orders concerning the guest-room near to Cousin Caroline's, and I prefer that you do not bother Cook. She has enough to do without unnecessary interruption. As you said yourself, there's no sense in keeping a dog . . .' He looked at Horatio in an absent-minded fashion, but received no response, and then went out again, firmly closing the door behind him.

Julia, visibly deflated by her half-brother's refusal to allow her to interfere in the running of the house, returned to her seat and said petulantly, 'He didn't even say that he'd called on your mama when he came home! Fancy forgetting that she was coming!'

Caroline herself wondered that he had made no previous mention of the visit, for he had had several opportunities to do so.

'What is she like?' Julia asked. 'Is she much like my own dear mama?'

From the eagerness in her voice, it was apparent to Caroline that she was hoping to find some compensation for the long absence of Lady Hartwell in the forthcoming meeting with her sister.

'I don't know,' she replied, 'for I've never seen your mother.'

'Did I not show you her portrait? How silly of me—I'm sure I meant to! Do come and see it now—there's plenty of time before dinner. And you must tell me all Aunt Barnes's little likes and dislikes, so that I may be sure to make her perfectly comfortable during her stay.'

Caroline thought privately that one hardly needed to know all a person's likes and dislikes for a one-night stay, but she went good-naturedly with Julia to see the portrait, assuring her that Mrs Barnes had no strong aversions or partialities in the matter of food, being accustomed to eating what was set before her in order to give a good example to her children in the matter of not being over-finicky—although she had words to say in her kitchen afterwards if a meal were not well-cooked and served.

Julia led the way to the library, which surprised Caroline, as she had not noticed a portrait there in her earlier visit, but this was understandable, as it hung in one of the alcoves and was far from well lit. It was a conventional study of a lady in a fashionable gown of some ten years earlier, which now looked extremely scanty and diaphanous, particularly on a plump matron past her first youth, whose dishevelled locks *à la Titus* framed a face which was tantalisingly like, yet unlike, that of Mrs Barnes.

'Is she much like?' Julia asked hopefully, looking from Caroline to the portrait and back again, as if also seeking a likeness between the two.

'Well, yes and no . . .' Caroline said cautiously. 'My Mama never dressed in high fashion, for City folk are—er—more conservative in their dress, and, of course, they will both have changed a great deal since that was painted, but—yes, I do believe they are alike, in the face at least. On the other hand, their lives have been so different, and that is bound to have affected their appearances. Mama has had eight children in all, and lost three of them . . . Such things affect the face, as well as the figure, you know!'

'I hope she may be like mama as I remember her!' Julia said fervently, sitting down at the table by the window and fixing her eyes on the dimly-lit portrait. 'I come in here sometimes, when I can't quite remember just how mama looked, and gaze at her picture to refresh my memory, but it's difficult, for she didn't really look like that when I last saw her, of course . . .'

She launched into a long monologue about her memories of her mother, and Caroline, listening with sympathetic patience, felt very sorry for her. She sat down at the opposite side of the table, and, for a few minutes, followed the flow of Julia's reminiscences, but it soon became apparent that she had no real need of an auditor, but was talking more for her own benefit than Caroline's, so the latter's attention gradually slipped away, although she maintained a pose of concentration and interest, idly running her thumb along the edges of a notebook which lay before her on the table.

There was no intention in her mind of looking inside the book, which was a thick, card-covered quarto notebook of ordinary appearance, with ROBERT HARTWELL written firmly on the front, but it happened that Julia, in demonstrating with her hands the length of her mother's hair when it was let down, almost overturned an inkwell, and as Caroline put out a hand to save it, she caught the edge of the book and it flipped open.

Naturally, she looked at the page before her, and was sufficiently puzzled by what she saw to look more closely. Most of the page was occupied by a drawing, little more than a line running from near the top to about two-thirds down the middle of the page, with other lines coming across from her right to join it, opening out a little as they did so, like rivers coming to the coast on a map.

A map! Of course—that's what it was, and the dots marked along the vertical line, each with a letter against it, must be towns on the coast!

But what coast? Which country did it represent? Assuming that the top of the page was north, what country had a very short east-to-west coast at its northern extremity, then a long west coast, broken by the mouths of three rivers, and then apparently petered out indeterminately to the south below a bulge around the mouth of the southernmost river, where a large L was emphatically underlined and ringed round . . .

Caroline's knowledge of geography was reasonably good for a young lady with no pretensions (or, indeed, desire) to be considered a blue-stocking, but it was a while before she noticed that the presumed western coastline continued sufficiently beyond what she had assumed to be the north coast to be a deliberate extension rather than an accident, which meant, she thought, that the 'north coast' was in fact, a border, not a coast, and another few seconds sufficed for her to recall a map which she had studied recently, and realise that this represented Portugal. It was only then that she looked at the few lines of neat writing at the foot of the page.

'Mondego the nearest practicable landing to L,' she read. 'Heavy surf. Admiral Cotton considers suitable.'

'What do you think, Cousin Caro?' Julia's voice cut into her thoughts, its tone changed from mournful reminiscence to eager questioning. 'I don't mind her having mama's room, if you think she might prefer it to the blue guest-room.'

Caroline flicked the book shut and replied tactfully, 'It's a very kind thought, Cousin Julia, but I'm sure Mama would not wish to put anyone to so much trouble just for one night. She will be perfectly comfortable in the guest-room, for she has a particular liking for blue.'

She was conscious of some surprise at her own quickness in guessing the content of Julia's original, unheard question, and the smoothness of her reply, which was of a nature likely to satisfy Julia and prevent her insisting on putting Mrs Barnes into Lady Hartwell's room—an eventuality which would be best avoided, as Caroline could imagine her mother's reactions to the cloying femininity and the profusion of knick-knacks she would find there.

Julia seemed to find unending matter for talk in the anticipated visit, and prattled about it throughout dinner and in the parlour afterwards, until Mr Hartwell, obviously finding her as irritating as ever, eventually begged her somewhat acidly to talk about something else, or, preferably, keep silence. Miffed, she chose the latter, and for half an hour remained firmly close-lipped, scowling at her embroidery, while Mr Hartwell read his news-sheet, Horatio snored, and Caroline felt increasingly uncomfortable. When bedtime came at last, Caroline was glad to escape to her room, to lie awake for some time, wondering what had made her mother decide to come to Canons Grange, and to worry about the possibility of some bad news which her parents might feel should be broken to her in person.

Oddly mixed up with this were vague thoughts about what she had seen in the notebook on the library table, and the memory suddenly flashed into her mind of something which had been written at the top of the page, which she had hardly noticed at the time—a date, 1st August, 1808.

She sat up in bed with a jerk. The first of August! But how could Mr Hartwell have known more than six weeks ago that Sir Arthur Wellesley would land at Mondego? Surely that was the actual day of the landing?

Concentrating, she tried to recall when she had first heard the news of the landing herself. Which day was it that her brother came in from the City so full of the news? Surely not until well into August?

Perhaps, had she more time to think about it, she might have remembered, and she might have become much more curious about Mr Hartwell's apparent second-sighted ability to know where the army of Portugal had landed on the very day it occurred, but her mind was much occupied with the anticipation of seeing her mother again after the longest separation from her which she had ever known (a whole week!) and she had experienced a trying day, what with one thing and another, so the matter of the notebook was soon forgotten in some more personal thoughts, and those, in turn, were lost in sleep.

CHAPTER
EIGHT

MRS BARNES had not viewed her elder daughter's foray
into the countryside with complacency, despite appearances to the contrary. She had a good opinion of
Caroline's common sense and intelligence, but had,
nevertheless, experienced misgivings about casting
her into the bosom of the Hartwell family of sufficient
strength to cause her a couple of disturbed nights between Caroline's departure from Stepney on Friday and
Mr Hartwell's brief call on Monday.

He had, however, assured her that Caroline had not
succumbed to despair or disease, and had considerably
relieved her anxiety by suggesting that she visit Canons
Grange to see for herself. His offer of a week or so's stay
was briskly whittled down to a single night, for Mrs
Barnes firmly declined to leave her household under
Alice's doubtful supervision for a longer period, and she
duly arrived at eleven o'clock on Friday morning with
her maid, driving up to the door in fine style in her
husband's recently-acquired bottle-green chaise, drawn
by four matched dapple greys and attended by two
outriders and a groom.

Julia, who seemed even more anxious than Caroline
for her to arrive, had been fidgeting about all morning,
constantly running to the parlour window to look out,
and even going part-way down the drive to see if any
sound of a carriage could be heard on the road. But the
sudden scrunching of wheels and hooves on the gravel
terrace caught her unawares in the end, and she ran out
to meet the chaise well behind Caroline and Horatio,
only to find that Mr Hartwell was before them all.

This surprised Caroline, who had thought he showed only a mildly polite interest in Mrs Barnes's visit, for he had disappeared in the direction of the stables after breakfast, and she had assumed that he was gone riding somewhere. However, when she came out of the front door to greet her mother, there he was, opening the door of the chaise, letting down the step and handing Mrs Barnes out almost before the groom had descended from his perch.

Caroline, moved by his unwelcome presence to recollect that she was no longer a child, checked her impulsive run towards the haven of her mother's arms and bobbed a little formal curtsy before sailing forward in a dignified manner to say, 'Dear Mama! How very good to see you again! Are you well? Did you have a pleasant journey?'

Mrs Barnes gave her daughter a quizzical look, and replied, 'Good morning, Caroline. You look to be in good health. Yes, I am well, and the journey was without mishap. You may kiss me.'

Caroline did so, curbing a strong desire to giggle, for her intercourse with her mother was normally rather less formal than this, and then she beckoned forward Julia, who was almost jigging with impatience in the background, but, before she could make a formal introduction, Julia burst out, 'Oh, you are so like my own dearest mama! I'm so happy to make your acquaintance, ma'am! Oh, dearest Aunt Barnes!'

She flung her arms about her aunt and kissed her warmly on both cheeks, knocking her bonnet awry. Mrs Barnes straightened it, raising her eyebrows a little at this ungenteel exhibition of exuberance, and said drily, 'You must be Miss Hartwell, I suppose. How d'you do?'

If this was intended to recall her niece to a more proper mode of behaviour, it failed, for Julia gave her another hug, and cried, 'Pray, call me Julia! Do think of me as if I were your own daughter, for you are my only aunt, and my dear Mama is so far away!' Then tears welled up in her eyes, but did not quite spill over.

Mrs Barnes was sufficiently moved to say, 'As you wish, dear Julia', and pat her bracingly on the shoulder, adding, 'You do remind me a little of my own Alice!', which only Caroline recognised as a back-handed compliment.

At this point, Horatio decided that his presence had been ignored for too long, and he uttered a series of sharp, pathetic yelps to get attention, then approached the newcomer with tail down, ears flopping sideways and the mournful expression of a dog which has not heard a kind word addressed to it for a month, besides being half-starved and generally ill-treated.

Mrs Barnes contemplated the wretched picture, and, unimpressed, enquired, 'Does this creature reside here?'

'That,' replied Mr Hartwell tersely, 'is Horatio. He was my dog, but he seems to have deserted me for your daughter. Do not, ma'am, allow him to bamboozle you into feeling sorry for him. If he claims to be put upon, he lies! Shall we go in? I'm sure you must be in need of refreshment after your journey.'

By the time chocolate had been served and partaken of with polite conversation, there was time before luncheon only for Mrs Barnes to inspect her room, which she approved with more spontaneity than she was wont to show, and to tidy herself before descending to the dining-room.

Caroline, who could judge her mother's opinions pretty well by her face and what she did *not* say, knew that this room did not meet with her approval at all, and, indeed, she did go so far as to say, looking at the dark panelling and heavy furniture, that she supposed Lord Hartwell liked to keep some parts of the house in their earlier appearance out of antiquarian interest. To which

Mr Hartwell blandly replied that he believed his father had something of the sort in mind. Julia uttered an unladylike snort and said that, in her opinion, the room had not been made habitable because the men of the family had no sensibilities and were quite blind to their surroundings, however hideous.

Mrs Barnes fixed her with the icy glance with which she habitually reduced Alice to propriety, and replied 'Indeed?' in a tone which killed the topic stone dead.

Julia behaved very well for the rest of the meal, not making a single unfortunate remark, or attempting to pick a quarrel with Mr Hartwell, or even raising her voice unbecomingly.

Unfortunately, any good impression made by this exertion of self-control was spoiled by an outburst of petulance as they rose from the table, occasioned by Mr Hartwell's proposal that Mrs Barnes and Caroline should take a stroll alone together in the garden.

'But there is so much I wish to ask Aunt Barnes!' Julia protested. 'It would surely be better if we sit in the parlour and talk. I'm sure it is damp and chill in the garden, and Aunt Barnes would rather stay indoors and tell me all about dearest Mama's childhood!'

'Mrs Barnes is here to visit her own daughter, not you,' Mr Hartwell replied scathingly. 'No doubt she may choose to spare you a little of her time later, but meanwhile, have the goodness to go about your own affairs elsewhere.'

To Caroline's surprise, Mrs Barnes put herself quite firmly on Mr Hartwell's side by saying, 'You are most considerate, sir! I should indeed welcome the opportunity of a little conversation with my daughter, and your gardens appear most attractive. A garden of any size is an amenity which, regrettably, residence in Stepney or the City has denied to me for many years.'

It was, of course, necessary for a lady of Mrs Barnes's

age and dignity to don bonnet and shawl before walking in the garden, and Caroline's feeling of indignation at her mother's support of the Enemy had lost its first sharpness by the time they were strolling along the neat paved paths, Horatio huffing at their heels. Nevertheless, she felt moved to say, 'You see how poor Cousin Julia is constantly set down by Mr Hartwell, Mama.'

'Miss Hartwell would be a much improved young lady if she had been consistently set down by everyone from birth!' Mrs Barnes replied with a touch of acidity. 'I've no doubt your aunt spoiled her, and her godmother has obviously continued the process instead of remedying it. I find it hardly surprising that her half-brother is moved to take a somewhat severe tone with her. Now, let us sit down on this bench, which appears to be clean, and you may tell me how you have been this past week.'

Caroline obediently sat beside her mother, remembering to keep her back straight and not lounge unbecomingly, and Horatio, after peering under the bench in the hopes of finding a villain, or at least a rat, settled himself to sleep at her feet. 'To tell truth,' she said pensively, 'I have thought several times of coming home, for the situation here is not at all comfortable, with the constant quarrelling between my cousins. However, I do feel very sorry for Cousin Julia, for she is very lonely and unhappy, and has never been taught to occupy herself at all, and Mr Hartwell finds fault with everything she does or says.'

'Do you wish to return to Stepney with me in the morning, then?' Mrs Barnes enquired in a neutral tone.

Caroline hesitated, biting her lip, and then replied, half-reluctantly, 'No, thank you. I think I shall remain for the month. Cousin Julia has many good characteristics, despite her unfortunate ones, and we are beginning to contrive to amuse ourselves pretty well while Mr Hartwell is away. Besides, there is a dinner-party planned, and it would put everything out if I left so suddenly, and there is to be a Harvest Supper . . .'

'So life in the country is not as crashingly boring as you expected?' Mrs Barnes enquired, smiling a little at Caroline's start of surprise at her use of such a colloquialism.

'Well, no. It does appear to have its good times!' Caroline admitted, smiling. 'There is pleasant and interesting society here, and I have already made some acquaintances in the neighbourhood.' She gave an account of the dinner at the Rectory, and the subsequent visit by Major Bridges and his friend.

Mrs Barnes nodded approvingly, watching Caroline's face as she talked, and then said, 'There is something which I think I should say to you. I did consider raising the matter before you left home, but there was little time, and the opportunity did not arise. However, now that you have begun to move a little in circles other than those to which you have been accustomed, it is fully time for me to speak about it.'

Caroline stirred uneasily, wondering what was to come.

'You must be aware,' she continued, 'that your father and I have in mind the need to seek a suitable marriage for you in the near future. Your father, naturally, thinks of it as a matter of business, and looks among his trade contacts for a suitable partner for you, but, to my view, this is an unnecessarily narrow outlook. I welcomed Mr Hartwell's invitation to you because it opened up a possibility for you to gain access to a wider field of acquaintance—to move, in short, into those circles of Society from which I come myself—the landed classes. Life can be restricted for the wife of a City merchant. I do not complain myself, mark you! My own life is contented and happy, and my marriage to your father all that I could desire, but there are many ladies of my acquaintance who find it otherwise! In short, Caroline, if you should happen to encounter a gentleman—an eligible gentleman, that is—during your visit here, to whom you feel sufficiently drawn to contemplate marriage with equanimity, and if he should show a similar interest, you need not fear that your father would be unsympathetic to his proposal.'

'But would not Papa prefer me to marry in the City?' Caroline enquired, detecting an inconsistency in what her mother had said.

'Your papa,' Mrs Barnes replied, giving her a very straight look, 'has no rigid opinions on family matters. His inclinations are capable of amelioration by reasonable persuasion. You will find,' she added with less formality, 'that the majority of men can be brought to see reason by the application of a little intelligent argument!' And she gave Caroline a meaningful smile, accompanied by the slightest flicker of one eyelid.

'Yes, Mama,' Caroline replied demurely.

'Now, as far as the Hartwells are concerned,' Mrs Barnes proceeded in her usual business-like fashion, 'I gather that you have taken a liking to Miss Hartwell, which pleases me, as I feel some responsibility towards her, as her aunt, despite the differences between my sister and me. However, I must warn you not to become prejudiced in her favour, for she is truly a most badly-brought-up young lady.'

'Yes, Mama, I do realise that,' Caroline replied earnestly, 'and I will do all I can to set her a good example, and perhaps even correct her at times, for she does seem inclined to take some notice of what I say. I do wish, however, that Mr Hartwell might be less overbearing and impatient with her. He plainly has a very poor opinion of the female sex in general!'

'Hardly surprising, when you consider the females with whom he has had the closest family contact!' Mrs

Barnes pointed out. 'My sister was ever the greatest ninny-hammer—your sister Alice is positively sensible by comparison! Lady Staveley does not appear to be a female likely to inspire respect in a man of intelligence. You should also bear in mind that Mr Hartwell has more than enough to worry about without the additional burden of a self-willed young lady without enough sense to fill a salt-spoon! Don't judge the man too harshly, Caroline. You may regret it when you know him better.'

Caroline made a non-committal reply, not wishing to appear so undutiful as to contradict her parent, and presently turned the conversation by enquiring for news of home, which led to an enjoyable chronicle of the doings of everyone in the Stepney household from Mr Barnes to the ginger cat, until a footman appeared to enquire if the ladies would care to take tea with Miss Hartwell in the parlour.

Julia appeared rather quelled and nervous when they rejoined her, and Caroline wondered if Mr Hartwell had spoken further to her on the subject of not pressing her demands upon Mrs Barnes, but that lady raised the matter herself as soon as the cups had been handed by enquiring, 'And what would you like me to tell you about your poor mama?'

Julia cheered up at once, and unleashed a flood of questions about her mother's childhood which Mrs Barnes seemed content to answer to the best of her ability with a lengthy reminiscence of happy (if rather uneventful) days in that golden past when life for the children of an English country landowner was untouched by the shadows of revolution and war.

Mr Hartwell, to Caroline's satisfaction, did not put in an appearance all afternoon to spoil Julia's enjoyment of this rare opportunity to hear about her mother from someone who had known her well before her marriage.

But, inevitably in her estimation, he marred the pervading air of contentment at dinner by asking, 'And have you been withindoors all day, Julia? Have you taken no exercise at all?'

'I consider it essential to good health that one should exercise in the open air every day, unless one is unwell, or the weather is too inclement,' Mrs Barnes commented. 'If you do not care to walk, my dear, could you not ride? Your dear mama was, at your age, very fond of riding.'

'I have no liking for it,' Julia replied, tossing her curls in a manner which reminded Caroline of a restive horse.

'My own girls have always taken what opportunities they may to ride,' Mrs Barnes continued inexorably. 'We all regret that it is not easy to do so regularly in Stepney.'

'Indeed?' exclaimed Mr Hartwell. 'I'm so sorry—I had no idea that Cousin Caroline liked to ride. Why did you not say?' This to Caroline. 'There are half a dozen horses eating their heads off in the stables, and two of them are broke to side-saddle! I'd be only too pleased to make you free of either of them. I know—come for a ride now, after dinner! There's plenty of time before dark, and you've not been further than the garden all day.'

Caroline, horrified, opened her mouth to refuse vehemently, but Mrs Barnes broke in before she could say a word with a brisk, 'What an excellent idea, and Julia shall take a turn about the gardens with me so that we may continue our talk together. You have your riding-habit with you, Caroline, and it will not take you above ten minutes to change.'

Such was Mrs Barnes's control over her family that Caroline did not think to demur, but went upstairs after dinner to change into the new dark green riding-habit which she had not yet worn, and the equally new and unsullied half-boots which went with it. The only comfort she derived was the certainty given by her mirror that the outfit was most becoming, with its hussar-style black frogging and the dashing little hat with a pale green ostrich-plume curling down at one side.

By the time she went downstairs again, two horses had been saddled and brought round to the front door, and Mr Hartwell was checking the girth of what looked like a brand-new side-saddle. He introduced Caroline's mount to her as 'Miranda—a five-year-old with a good temperament. You'll need to hold her in if anything startles her, but otherwise she'll give you no trouble.'

Caroline patted the mare's neck dubiously and, with a feeling of fatalistic reluctance, allowed Mr Hartwell to assist her to mount, which he did by clasping her firmly at the waist and lifting her, without apparent effort, on to her saddle. She settled herself into place, arranged her skirts, and licked her lips nervously, looking round to see if her mother was at hand to be appealed to for a reprieve, but Mrs Barnes had already taken Julia away for an extensive stroll through the shrubberies.

'We'll go along the ridge towards the Forest,' Mr Hartwell said as they set out. 'There's an hour before dark, and it's a pleasant ride along the higher ground. I wish I'd known earlier that you like to ride, for it's always more enjoyable to have a companion.'

He seemed to be in buoyantly good spirits, and looked about him as if the mild evening, gilded by the descending sun, had been devised for his particular delectation. Caroline, on the other hand, had no eye for the beauties of nature, but concentrated all her attention on remembering everything she had been taught in her riding-lessons, from holding the reins correctly and not too tightly to keeping her back straight in its uncomfortable twisted position, and her weight squarely in the middle of her saddle. Most of all, she tried not to look down, for the ground was alarmingly far below her.

Mr Hartwell did not appear to notice her lack of response to his comments on the view, the mildness of the evening, and the wealth of bird-song, every bird within miles being apparently determined to perform its entire repertoire before sundown. Having failed to elicit any more than the briefest of replies to those remarks, he gave an enlivening dissertation on the success of the recent harvest, pointed out Pinnacles to their right, and finally, as they came to the very edge of the Forest, remarked, 'Damnation! Ferdinand appears to have gone lame!'

Caroline was jerked out of preoccupation by the expletive, and then realised that her companion had checked his horse and dismounted. She tugged hopefully at her own reins and succeeded in stopping Miranda, who had in any case slowed down and turned her head to see what had become of her stable-mate, and was not averse to ambling back to rejoin him.

'It's only a stone caught under the edge of the shoe,' Mr Hartwell said in a relieved tone, peering at the upturned near-side hoof which was resting against his braced leg. 'I can get it out with the implement thoughtfully provided by the maker of my pocket-knife.'

He groped in his pocket and pulled out a clasp-knife. She watched with interest as he deftly inserted the hooked blade under the edge of the iron shoe, and quite forgot that she was perched insecurely on a very large horse at an inordinate and frightening height above the ground. Neither did she notice that Miranda, who had been enjoying the gentle trot along the ridge and resented having to stand about while her owner did something inexplicable to Ferdinand, was beginning to twitch her ears and fidget.

A squirrel darted out of a nearby bush, checked abruptly at the sight of intruders, then ran almost across

Miranda's front hooves to reach the safety of its own particular tree, where it scolded shrilly from a high branch. The mare bucked and jumped as the darting form shot past under her nose, and Caroline, almost unseated, made a convulsive grab at both reins and mane, which did nothing to calm her mount. Miranda uttered an indignant squeal and took off at full gallop into the mysterious depths of the Forest.

Caroline managed somehow to retain her seat and her grip on the reins, but she was quite incapable of checking Miranda's flight, for she had no idea what to do. Common sense told her that a low branch might easily knock her off, or even break her neck, so she flattened herself along the mare's neck, put both arms round it, and hung on, her cheek pressed against the rough hair of the mane, and her eyes on the bushes and bracken flying past so far below her.

'Please let her stop soon!' she prayed. 'Please don't let me fall off!'

Miranda sped along a barely discernible track, then suddenly emerged into a broad ride where half a dozen sturdy ponies stood in a companionable group, watched over by a man sitting comfortably with his back against a tree and his battered straw hat tilted over his eyes. He had heard Miranda's hooves pounding along the track, and as she entered the ride, he pushed back his hat, jumped to his feet, and stood ready. She checked at the sudden sight of the ponies, flung up her head, and no doubt would have jinked and taken off in a different direction, but the man ran forward and caught her harness close to her mouth, pulled her nose down, and said soothingly, 'There now—stand quiet, gel! There's me good Mirandy, then! Come to yer old friend then, that's me beauty!'

Miranda, obviously recognising his voice, pricked up the ears which had been flattened against her head, snuffled out the last of her fright, and stood quiet, her flanks heaving gently. Then she offered the man a front hoof, as if to shake hands, but put it down again when he did not take it. Caroline managed to pull herself upright, then slid out of her saddle, landing on the ground on her feet, more by luck than intent.

'Thank goodness you were here!' she said breathlessly. 'I'm so grateful to you for stopping her!'

'Run orf with yer leddy, did yer?' the man enquired of the mare in a matter-of-fact tone. 'Bad gel, Mirandy! Yer did ought ter be shamed on yerself, so yer did! Mester 'Artwell'll hev a thing or three ter say ter yer, shouldn't wonder!'

Caroline, half-leaning against Miranda's shoulder and waiting for her own breathing to return to normal and her legs to become sufficiently steady to support her, wondered who the man could be. He was fairly tall and very broad-shouldered, his powerful chest and heavily-muscled arms straining the buttons and seams of his rough jacket. He had a saturnine face with a bold, gipsyish look to it, and he clearly had a way with animals, for Miranda was positively fawning upon him as he talked to her, repeatedly offering him one or other of her front hooves. What on earth could he be doing here, in the middle of the Forest, with six ponies?

The fresh sound of approaching hooves turned all heads, equine and human, towards the track from which Miranda and Caroline had emerged so precipitately, and Mr Hartwell appeared on Ferdinand, who was cantering with no sign of lameness.

'Ah, there you are, Cousin Caroline!' Mr Hartwell said briskly. 'Good evening, Will.'

'Evening, Mester 'Artwell.' The man nodded as to an almost equal. 'Summat fritted Mirandy, did it? She came out o' the trees like a Derby winner!'

'A squirrel,' Mr Hartwell replied, looking searchingly

at Caroline, who was feeling, and no doubt looking, a little pale, but was now standing unsupported and giving some attention to the straightness of her hat and the fall of her skirts. 'Stopped her, did you? I'm obliged to you.'

'No trouble, mester. The young leddy did well ter stay on. Had the sense to lie flat so's not ter be knocked orf by a tree-branch.'

'Yes, very sensible.' Mr Hartwell dismounted and walked round Miranda, viewing her from various angles, but glancing frequently at Caroline.

'She's not hurt,' the man volunteered. 'Not even winded.'

'No, thank goodness,' Mr Hartwell said. 'Well, we'd best be going home before we're overtaken by the dark. Are you ready, Cousin?' He was looking at the man as he spoke, and handing him something which clinked a little, so did not notice the expression on Caroline's face.

'Yes,' she managed shakily, and submitted to being put up on Miranda's back again. She turned to thank the man, but he and his ponies had silently disappeared into the darkness of the Forest, and were nowhere to be seen.

'You gave me quite a fright, going off like that,' Mr Hartwell remarked conversationally as he led the way back along the track. 'It was bad luck that the squirrel ran so close under the mare's feet. She's a good mare normally, but something like that would spook almost any horse! You did well to control her. I suppose you meant to let her run off her fright?'

'I—I couldn't stop her,' Caroline admitted in an unsteady voice. 'I didn't control her at all. I just held on and tried not to fall off. I've never galloped before.'

'Never . . . ?' he echoed in incredulous tones. 'Good heavens! But I thought . . . Your mother said . . .'

'Alice and I have riding-lessons occasionally,' she said ruefully, 'but on an elderly and rather stout pony on Stepney Green. We take turns to sit on him and walk round, and sometimes we trot. I've never ridden a full-sized horse before. I'm sorry—I should have told you the truth before we set out, but I felt so foolish, after Mama said that I love to ride.'

'I can only say that you've been well taught, for I had no idea . . . I saw nothing amiss in the way you were riding before we met the squirrel. In fact, I had observed to myself that you have a good seat. Thank God that you came to no harm on your first gallop!'

Caroline smiled a little uncertainly, feeling an unexpected glow of pleasure at his comments on her riding ability, and told herself that a compliment was a compliment, and was not totally devalued by being voiced in a matter-of-fact tone by a man one disliked. She settled herself into her saddle with more confidence, and quite enjoyed the gentle trot home, even observing the lovely pale green above the after-glow in the western sky.

'If you don't mind,' she said as they clattered on to the cobbles of the stableyard, 'I'd rather nothing was said to Mama about Miranda running away with me. She really does believe I can ride well, and it would only alarm her.'

'By all means,' Mr Hartwell replied conspiratorily. 'Not a word, I promise!' He lifted her down from Miranda's back, and held her for a moment, his hands still clasping her waist in a firm grip, and added quietly, 'You're a plucky lass as well as a sensible one! I find much to admire in you, *Caro mia*!' Caroline made some incoherent reply, and went indoors with something of a rush, feeling quite flustered.

They found Mrs Barnes and Julia enjoying an agreeable tête-à-tête over the teacups, and no mention was made of their expedition, apart from a conventional 'Did you enjoy your ride?' from Mrs Barnes.

She left soon after breakfast the next morning, and

Caroline had time for only a few minutes' private conversation with her before her departure, but Mrs Barnes made a point of saying, 'Bear in mind what I said to you about the possibility of meeting an eligible man in this vicinity, but don't feel obliged to view every man you encounter with an eye to marriage. Your situation is not so desperate that you must positively hunt for a husband! I'm glad that you've made up your mind to stay here for Julia's sake, and I'm sure you'll do your best by her, but if you find you are not happy or comfortable and wish to come home, be sure to write to your father, and he will send for you at once.'

Caroline thanked her warmly for this thoughtful reassurance, and accompanied her to her chaise with a string of messages for her family and friends at home. All too soon the green chaise jerked into motion and bowled rapidly away down the winding drive, Caroline running behind to the first bend for a last wave before it vanished from sight.

'How kind dearest Aunt Barnes was to tell me so much about dearest Mama!' Julia exclaimed. 'I'm so glad that she decided to visit us, and I hope she will soon come again.'

Having apparently made up his mind to be Caroline's dog, Horatio attached himself to her from then on, whenever he was allowed to do so, and padded about behind her at every opportunity, his claws clicking on the boards about the house, and his tongue lolling as if to assist him in keeping up when she walked abroad.

Caroline was embarrassed about the defection, but Mr Hartwell accepted the change of loyalties philosophically, and when she made some attempt at an apology, he replied, 'Oh, think nothing of it! He was always remarkably sensible for a dog, and it shows that he's also a creature of discernment and good judgment. He normally evinces a strong aversion to villains, so if you happen to meet one on your walks, you may be sure he'll do his best to defend you.'

As it happened, the first person who was a stranger to him whom Horatio encountered while out with Caroline was Mr Bell, and he treated him with great suspicion, sniffing about his feet in a derogatory fashion, and growled quite horridly when Mr Bell essayed a friendly word.

Mr Bell shrugged the rebuff aside but kept a wary eye on Horatio during the rest of his short conversation with Caroline, and the dog kept an equally wary eye on him, obviously regarding him as the sort of man who might kick a person if not carefully watched.

Caroline, as it happened, was out for a walk on her own the day after her mother's departure. It had rained the previous afternoon, and, although the day was fine, Julia had insisted on going to church that morning in the carriage, saying that the paths would be unpleasantly muddy, and, despite Caroline's determination not to spend another day indoors listening to her cousin squabbling with Mr Hartwell, she had been unable to persuade Julia to come out with her in the afternoon. So she had put on her boots, pinned up her frock to her ankles, and set out alone but for Horatio, Mr Hartwell having disappeared into the library after luncheon and firmly shut the door behind him.

By the time they met Mr Bell, Horatio had ceased to be a white dog from the midway contour downwards, and even his upper part was spotted with mud, and Caroline's skirts were somewhat draggled as well, but she persevered with her exercise, keeping to the higher ground, and, soon after parting from Mr Bell, she came in sight of the fantastical edifice which she had seen on the day of her arrival in Woodham, which she recalled was the residence of Lord and Lady Cressing.

The path which she had been following had run along
the top of the ridge above Canons Grange towards the
Forest, and then veered off to the right to descend into
the narrow valley of a stream, which it crossed by a
wooden bridge, before climbing again across a field
dotted with sheep, to join another path which skirted the
very edge of the Forest.

The presence of sheep led her to believe that she
might be on Lord Cressing's land, as she recalled that
Mr Hartwell had said that the Viscount kept them,
and she was just wondering if he would object to her
trespassing when another person emerged from the
Forest and started to come down the path towards
her, accompanied by a small grey shadow which
appeared to be fastened in some way at a distance of
about a foot from his heel.

Horatio, who had already shown some apparent confusion of identities in taking Mr Bell for a villain, now
confirmed Caroline's suspicions concerning his powers
of judgment by galloping off to greet the approaching
man as a friend, wagging his tail so hard that he over-
balanced, and bouncing happily about the shadow,
which proved, on closer inspection, to be a whippet.

'Good day, ma'am,' said the man, nodding familiarly,
although he did doff his rabbit-skin cap. 'Miss Barnes,
ain't it? I seed you in the bramble wood t'other day wi'
Mester 'Artwell and Miss Julia, though I reckon you
didn't see me!'

'Oh, yes,' Caroline replied non-committally. 'I think
this is Lord Cressing's land, is it not? Will he mind, do
you think, if I walk across it?'

'Not so long as 'Orace 'ere don't chase no sheep.
'Orace and me is old friends. 'Twas me give 'im 'is first
coney. A dog don't forget a thing like that.'

'Coney?' Caroline queried, not being sure what that
might be.

'Rabbit,' the man enlarged. 'I be Lord Cressing's warrener—coney-keeper. Warrener by name and by trade!'

'Oh, I see. I suppose your ancestors were warreners too, then?'

'Ar. Father to son, like. From Lunnon, ain't you? Ever seed a fitch?'

'A—a fitch? No, I don't believe I have . . .' Caroline had no idea what a fitch was either, but she was soon enlightened. Mr Warrener delved into the large pocket of his coat and pulled out a bundle of creamy-white fur, which unrolled into a long, narrow, sinuous animal with a wedge-shaped head, little hard red eyes, and a mouthful of wickedly sharp teeth.

'This is Phoebe,' Mr Warrener said, smoothing the animal lovingly. 'Named after me sister, in cause of she looks like 'er, only me sister's dark-haired. Good little beast she is, only mind she don't bite you!'

Caroline cautiously stroked Phoebe's head, which the fitch did not object to particularly, and he then returned her to his pocket.

'I suppose I should put Horatio on a leash, because of the sheep,' she said. 'But I haven't so much as a piece of string about me.'

''Orace won't chase no sheep,' Mr Warrener replied confidently. 'Bin well-trained, 'as 'Orace. Mester 'Artwell knows 'ow to train a dog, or a norse, or a nelephant, probably. Got a way wi' animals, 'as Mester 'Artwell. Animals knows when a man's got a good 'eart and a strong mind, and they take notice of 'im. You've got a good 'eart yerself, so 'Orace takes to you, and 'e'll do as you say in cause of 'e likes you. Look at 'im now—telling my Dodger about you, like as not!'

Horatio was sitting nose to nose with the whippet, apparently communing, but he glanced up at Mr Warrener when his name was mentioned, as did

Dodger, and both acknowledged their mention with their tails.

'Got ter get on,' Mr Warrener said, looking up at the sun. 'Any time you want a fur lining to yer cloak, or a muff, you let me know—got a good lot of skins to choose from, and me wife'll make 'em up.'

'Thank you—I'll remember that,' Caroline replied. 'Oh—just one thing . . .' remembering something which had puzzled her earlier. 'What is an effer? Can you tell me?'

'That'd be what the gentry calls a heifer,' he replied solemnly, sounding the h very firmly. 'It's a cow what ain't 'ad 'er first calf yet. Good day to you.'

'Thank you, and good day to you,' Caroline replied, and went on her way up the hill, wondering if Horatio would follow her, or desert her for Mr. Warrener. A steady grumbling sound at her heels soon reassured her that she would not have to confess to Mr Hartwell on her return that she had lost his dog as well as alienating its affections.

Horatio ceased to grumble once the path levelled off, and appeared to like the way along the edge of the Forest. The path led along the foot of the terraced gardens of Pinnacles, and then went on towards a row of cottages and a road, on which Caroline could see a wagon and a carrier's cart, but she decided at that point to turn back, and arrived home an hour or so later, tired in body, but much refreshed in spirit by the fresh air and the peace of the countryside, which she decided was not nearly as unpleasant as she had expected it to be.

CHAPTER
NINE

As BEFORE, Mr Hartwell left Canons Grange on his journey very early in the morning, before Caroline or Julia was awake, and Julia's temper showed such an immediate improvement at his absence that she even volunteered to walk into Woodham with Caroline and ask the Rector if they might look at the interior of the church, which was kept locked when there was no service.

The Rector was from home, but Lord and Lady Cressing were at the Rectory, and offered to show Caroline the church, much to the obvious relief of Mrs Calvert and Julia, who settled to a comfortable cose over chocolate, attended hopefully by Frederick, who, to judge by his girth, was fond of cream.

Lucinda, being the Rector's daughter, knew a great deal about the church, and told Caroline something of its history as they walked about the interior. She pointed out the large tomb by the chancel of a member of the family which bought the Abbey lands from King Henry, and commented that the poor man and his wife looked most uncomfortable, for both were lying stiffly on narrow shelves, one above the other, he in full armour, and she in a starched ruff and cap and voluminous black skirts, with their children kneeling piously below them.

Lord Cressing said that he much preferred the tomb on the other side of the chancel, and so did Caroline. It was a handsome piece of work in white marble, commemorating a sea-captain, and was carved with the instruments of his trade—quadrant and compass, astrolabe and hour-glass, and, more sinisterly, dirk, cutlass, pistol and cannon.

'Where were the Abbots buried?' asked Caroline, who had expected to see at least a few ecclesiastical memorials, but could find none.

'In the part that was pulled down,' Lucinda replied. 'This part was always the parish church, you see, and the other two-thirds belonged to the canons. Would you like to ascend the tower? It's worth going up for the view, although the ascent isn't easy.'

'I should like it very much,' Caroline replied, 'if you don't mind, that is, for I've no wish to be any trouble.'

'Not in the least,' Lord Cressing said at once. 'I mean to go up in any case, to see if Howe has mended the stay on Charity. Have you the key, Lucy?'

Lucinda sorted through the large bunch of keys which she was carrying, selected a small one, and unlocked an unobtrusive little black door in the north-west corner of the church. It gave on to a narrow spiral staircase, lit by occasional slit windows, up which she led the way, followed by Caroline, and then by Lord Cressing, who proposed to catch whichever of them should fall, as the stairs were worn and uneven in height.

The climb was quite steep, but an old bell-rope had been strung along the outer wall as a hand-rail, allowing the climbers to pull themselves up more easily, and the climb was broken by occasional little landings before odd doors, at which Lucinda paused to say what was behind them.

'That's a cupboard,' she said of the first one. 'That goes on to the north aisle roof,' at the second, and 'Do just look through this', at the third, 'but hold on, for you may turn giddy!'

Caroline climbed the three very steep steps up to the door, opened it gingerly, and peered through. A narrow, well-lit passage faced her, and it was a moment before she realised that it was the clerestory. She took a cautious step or two along it, holding on to the wall, and looked down into the church, the floor of which was quite fifty feet below.

'Don't be alarmed,' Lord Cressing said from close behind her.

'Oh, I'm not!' Caroline replied. 'It gives such an impression of the size of the building. How ever did they manage to make such a great place all those hundreds of years ago?'

'With difficulty, one imagines!' Lord Cressing replied. 'In fact, I believe they took their scaffolding up with them, and had every piece of stone cut to size and shape on the ground, and, of course, passages like this were put in to help them to inspect and repair the fabric later.'

He offered Caroline his hand to guide and steady her as she turned in the narrow space and stepped back and down to where Lucinda was waiting, and the latter then led the way along a tiled passage to the ringing-chamber.

'I've heard the bells ringing,' Caroline said, looking at the eight ropes with their colourful sallies. 'They sound very sweet from Canons Grange.'

'Distance lends enchantment,' Lucinda said cheerfully. 'They're deafening in the Rectory! Now, can you manage the next part, do you think? I should leave your shawl and reticule here—they'll be quite safe.'

Caroline did as she was advised, for the next part of the ascent involved a very steep flight of wooden steps, little more than a ladder, braced against one wall, but with no guard-rail, and it was necessary for Lord Cressing to go first to open the heavy trap-door at the top. Lucinda went next, holding on to the steps as she climbed, and Caroline copied her, arriving safely at the top in the clock-chamber, where a sonorous tocking was all that was discernible of the clock, the room being pitch dark.

'Just a moment—stand still, or you may trip over something,' said Lord Cressing from the darkness. 'What on earth! Oh, it's bolted, that's all. There—now we can see', and a small shutter opened on the far side of the chamber, admitting a dim light through a glazed aperture to one side of the clock dial.

'I think we'd better wait for a moment,' Lord Cressing said, peering at something in his hand. 'If my watch is right . . .' there was a loud whirring from the clock mechanism '. . . it's about to strike.'

Whatever else he might have said was lost in a further whirring as the clock worked itself into a passion and ting-tanged the four quarters in a very forthright fashion, followed by a definite statement that the hour was ten, which caused the solid timbers under Caroline's feet to tremble slightly. The noise was quite stunning.

'I'm sorry,' Lord Cressing said when the sound had ceased and the last reverberations died to a whisper. 'I should have taken note of the time while we were still in the ringing-chamber. I'll just go up and open the door at the top, and then you'll be able to see the bells.'

He disappeared up another solid ladder-like construction, and presently was heard wrestling with something recalcitrant, for he said, 'Why the devil can't somebody put a drop of oil on this?' Then a comparative flood of light broke through the cut-away area of the bell-chamber floor where the ladder passed through, making it quite easy for the two ladies to ascend to a small area of staging just above the level of the bells.

'There they are—the voices of Woodham!' said Lord Cressing lovingly, coming down to join them, 'Aren't they beauties? You'll not see many finer, not in any tower in the country! Now, you've heard James and John and Gabriel already, for they're the clock bells. See, James and John are in the middle, numbers four and five. The treble there is Faith, Hope and Charity are two and three, and Michael and Raphael are over there, six and seven. The fine great beauty here, which is up, is Gabriel, the tenor. He weighs seventeen hundred-weight!'

Caroline found that she was looking over the rail of the small platform straight down into the mouth of a bell far larger than she had ever imagined a bell could be, for she had never been so close to one before.

'It's enormous!' she exclaimed. 'I had no idea! Is it the biggest bell in England?'

'No, and nowhere near it!' Lord Cressing replied. 'Great Tom at Westminster weighs sixty-two hundred-weight, but our little Gabriel's a fine bell, even if he's not in the largest category. Size isn't everything. It's more important that the tone and tune are good, and there aren't many to beat our ring for that!'

'He's been ringing for a whole year now,' Lucinda confided to Caroline in a mischievous tone. 'So he knows *all* about bells, of course!'

Lord Cressing ignored this remark, and ushered the ladies up the rest of the ladder and out on to the roof of the tower, the edge of which was guarded by a waist-high parapet, so there was no cause for anyone to feel at all nervous. The view was, in fact, no better than that from the poplar tree above Canons Grange, for the top of the tower was not as high, but it was interesting, for one could look down on the churchyard and the roofs of town. Lucinda pointed out Julia and her own mother, seated in the Rectory garden, with a small black and white figure stretched out in the sun at their feet.

Further afield, the buildings of the powder-mill could be seen, well spread out amid areas of grass and trees, which Caroline supposed was for reasons of safety rather than aesthetics. Between the mill and the town, she could see the stream from which she had rescued the young poacher, which disappeared under West Street and reappeared to the south of a large building which she deduced must be the silk-mill. She could also see the course of the Cornmill stream, which was running fast and deep across the ford before the church, for the mill was working and the grinding-stones could be heard quite clearly.

'What are those patches of cloth on the field beyond the silk-mill?' she asked. 'It looks like a tenting-ground, but the cloth is the wrong colour for linen.'

'It's silk,' Lucinda replied. 'See, there's an armed guard patrolling between the lengths, for it's too valuable to leave unwatched. Come round to the north side and you'll see the army camp.'

'The lengths a female will go to for a glimpse of a red coat!' Lord Cressing remarked to the gilded weathercock above their heads.

The camp was at some distance to the north of the town, and looked like a child's large toy from their vantage-point. The wooden barrack huts stood in neat rows about a sanded parade-ground, in the midst of which the bright flag flew from a white pole, and toy soldiers were grouped about in military formations, moving in a somewhat clockwork fashion.

'Their coats look to be mainly a dark colour from here,' Caroline remarked à propos Lord Cressing's last speech. 'Are they green?'

'I believe some of the Rifle Brigade may be in transit from here to there,' Lord Cressing replied off-handedly, 'But I should keep that under your very fetching bonnet, if you will.'

'Oh. Yes, of course.' Caroline was a little disconcerted. 'Do you think . . . ? Oh, but anyone who wished to know has only to walk along the edge of the Forest, or across the fields by the camp.'

'Indeed,' Lord Cressing replied. 'To tell truth, we had trouble here last year over a French spy, and I suppose those of us who knew about him have been a little suspicious of strangers since then. People who ride or walk along the high ground overlooking the camp or the powder-mill, you know, or who ask questions about them . . . You haven't by any chance encountered the mysterious Mr Bell again, have you? I ask because you seem to be the only person in the town who's actually spoken to him.'

'Well, yes, I have!' she said, feeling reluctant to speak about Mr Bell, for her acquaintance with him was, she felt, unconventionally informal. 'I've come across him a couple of times, but he's not shown any interest in the camp or the mill. I understand that he's only recruiting his health—he does look very sallow.' She paused, thinking and biting her lip, then went on slowly, 'I'm sure it's not at all proper that I should mention this, but Mr Hartwell's activities seem a little—well—odd—to me.'

'In what way?' Lord Cressing gave her a searching look.

'He seems to go off somewhere for a few days at frequent intervals, but he doesn't talk about where he's been, or what he's been doing. I'm sorry—I shouldn't talk so about my host, but it does seem a little strange, and as you mentioned . . .'

'Spies? No, your cousin Robert is not a spy, I assure you! You were right to mention your suspicions, though, for he might well have been one, if he were not— otherwise. Why don't you ask him where he goes, and why? He might tell you!'

'It's not my business,' Caroline replied soberly. 'I wish I'd not mentioned him.'

'But you were right to do so, if you thought his behaviour suspicious,' Lucinda said gently. 'The lives of a great many men could be put at risk by someone not speaking up when they had a suspicion about someone.

Suppose those men down there were about to go overseas, and a spy found out and let Bonaparte know. He could send ships to intercept them and sink their transports, and they could all be killed!'

Neither her husband nor Caroline pointed out that Bonaparte had found it difficult to send ships anywhere since Trafalgar, for the basic theme of her statement was undeniably true, and Caroline was comforted to think that any loyalty she owed to Mr Hartwell was outweighed by a greater loyalty to the men marching about on the parade-ground, and the flag flying above their heads.

After they had spent a little more time on the tower, they descended and joined Mrs Calvert and Julia in the Rectory garden, where they found Major Bridges and Captain Marsh arrived before them, and filled with zeal to protect the two young ladies on their dangerous walk home across the fields to Canons Grange.

'I'm sure we need not put you to such trouble . . .' Caroline began, after gratefully accepting a cup of coffee from Mrs Calvert, but Julia protested that she was quite dreadfully afraid of the pigs which they were bound to encounter by the Cornmill stream.

'But we need not go that way!' Caroline was being purposely obtuse, for, although she approved Major Bridges's interest in Julia, she felt reluctant to do anything to encourage Captain Marsh's attentions to herself. She was sure he was a most worthy and gallant young officer, but she had not the slightest wish to engage his affections.

'In that case, there will be cows,' countered Major Bridges resourcefully, 'and cows are notoriously given to jostling young ladies in order to eat the trimming from their bonnets. I should not like to hear, Miss Barnes, that your very charming bonnet had suffered such an injury through any lack of assistance from the Military!'

There was, of course, no possibility of refusing a military escort after that without being downright impolite, so Caroline acquiesced meekly, and she and Julia were duly escorted home, where Julia upset Cook and delighted the officers by inviting them to luncheon. Captain Marsh rather tactlessly said that any food was better than that served in the mess, but this was correctly interpreted by Julia as a compliment, and duly passed on to Cook, who was a little mollified thereby.

Two nights later, being a healthy young female who had taken a good walk in the fresh air during the day, Caroline fell asleep quickly, but was troubled by dreams, from one of which she half-woke with the feeling that she had heard voices somewhere near by.

'What an odd dream,' she thought, turning over, but was suddenly wide awake, for a low voice spoke again, saying something like, 'This one, I think', followed by a sharp crack.

She liked to sleep with a window slightly open in all but the worst weather, despite awful warnings about the dangers of the practice, and she realised that the sounds were coming from outside, beneath her window. She slipped out of bed, flung her shawl round her, and went to the window to look down. She could see nothing, but further sounds were identifiable as two voices speaking very quietly just inside an open window immediately below her own.

'The library,' she thought. 'Someone has broken into the library! Two people. They must be burglars!'

Her first instinct was to rouse the household, but she hardly knew how to set about it, for, with Mr Hartwell away, she had no idea of the location of the sleeping-quarters of any male person. It would be useless to call Julia, who would probably have hysterics and alarm the robbers, giving them time to get away in the confusion.

Presumably the servants slept on the floor above, but what if she blundered on a maid instead of one of the men? Then she thought that perhaps what she had heard was only a couple of servants creeping back into the house after an illicit outing in the master's absence . . .

At that moment she remembered the 'secret' staircase which led from the passage outside her room to the library, where it was concealed behind an 'invisible' door. She could creep down that, listen at the bottom, determine whether the intruders were burglars or servants, and then if necessary, return and raise the alarm.

It took only a few moments to light a candle with the tinder-box thoughtfully provided at her bedside, put on a wrapper with her shawl over it, seize the poker from the hearth, and steal as silently as possible, barefoot, out of her room in search of the door to the staircase. She was a minute or two finding it, for it was well concealed, but eventually her fingers touched the little brass knob, the door opened silently, and she began her cautious descent of the stairs, leaving the door open at the top.

This proved to be a mistake. She had almost reached the bottom of the stairs when her candle, which had been flickering, blew out, and she thought to herself, quite calmly, that the window of the library must still be open, causing a draught on the stairs. It was now pitch dark, save for a very faint patch of grey where the little window opened in the outer wall, but she thought that, as she was now on the next to last step, she might as well go to the bottom and listen before groping her way up again.

Unfortunately, she had miscalculated. There was one more step than she had remembered, and when, thinking she was at the bottom, she stepped forward, her foot descended another eight or nine inches, throwing her off-balance. She pitched sideways, dropping her candle-stick with a clatter, and fell against the door into the library. The latch gave way with a loud click.

CHAPTER
TEN

'WHAT THE DEVIL?' exclaimed a startled voice. There was the sound of quick footsteps, and the door was jerked wide open before Caroline could recover her balance, and she half-stumbled, half-fell, straight into the embrace of one of the intruders, who took a firm grip on her and exclaimed, 'Now, how on earth do you come to be falling out of the wall? Do you make a habit of listening at keyholes?' in a tone of mingled surprise and amusement, but Caroline heard only the surprise and assumed the other to be sarcasm, for it was Mr Hartwell!

'Well, how was I to know it was you?' she enquired a trifle sharply, disengaging herself from his arms and feeling distinctly foolish and ruffled. 'I heard someone breaking in, so I came to see who it was. I didn't want to rouse the household if it was only a couple of servants creeping in late. As for the wall—why, there's a staircase that comes down from just outside my room.' She gestured with the poker, which was still gripped in her right hand.

'I'd forgotten about that,' he said thoughtfully, eyeing the poker. 'That's how you came to be in here the other morning, I suppose? What was the poker for? You didn't intend to take on the burglars single-handed, I trust?'

'Of course not. It was just in case . . .'

'. . . you fell out of the wall,' he finished for her. 'Did you really think we were burglars?'

'I'm not accustomed to households where the master breaks into his own library in the middle of the night!' Caroline informed him frostily.

'No, I suppose it doesn't happen in a well-conducted household. I'm very sorry that we disturbed and alarmed you.' Mr Hartwell had the grace to show a proper contrition at last, but there ensued an awkward silence, for he said nothing more, but just stood looking at her.

Caroline, conscious of her flimsy nightshift and wrapper, her hair falling about her shoulders and her bare feet, looked about the room in order to avoid meeting his gaze.

The room was dimly lit by two branches of candles on the desk by the window, which, although they were out of the line of the draught, flickered enough to send grotesque shadows dancing about the walls. The other man, who had not spoken, was standing by the window, as if he had reacted to her arrival by making for the exit. As Caroline's eyes moved towards him, he turned his head away, but in doing so, he showed her his unmistakable profile, which the candles echoed in shadow caricature against the curtains behind him.

Before she could say anything, Mr Hartwell, following the direction of her gaze, said, 'Oh, forgive me —may I present Mr Childers?' There was the slightest hesitation between the title and the name, but Caroline did not need that to tell her that the name was false. 'We had a little business to discuss, so we came here to talk in comfort, but I didn't wish to disturb the whole house, so we entered—er—informally . . . My cousin, Miss Barnes, Mr Childers.'

Caroline made a small, demure curtsy, murmuring, 'Mr Childers', with a slight emphasis on the name, and the man made a somewhat curt bow in reply, but did not speak, and immediately stepped back further into the shadows.

'I'll not keep you from your business any longer, then,' Caroline said briskly. 'Perhaps I shall meet Mr Childers again in the morning?'

'I think not,' Mr Hartwell replied smoothly. 'He has to be on his way again almost immediately—to Yorkshire, you know. A long way.'

'Indeed,' Caroline replied. 'I'm sorry I disturbed you.'

'Oh, not at all!' he said earnestly. 'I admire your courage in coming to see what was going on. I'm most grateful to you for your concern. Oh, is that your candle? I thought you could not have come down in the dark.'

He picked up the dropped candlestick, relit the candle, and gave it to Caroline, who returned up the narrow stairs, conscious that he was standing at the bottom watching her.

'Good night, Caroline,' he said softly as she reached the top, and she found herself replying, 'Good night, Robert,' without thinking.

A wave of hot colour flooded through her whole body, and she hastily closed the door on the stairs and the man at the foot of them, and stood leaning against the panelling, telling herself with a confused but desperate attempt at calm common sense that there was no possibility that he could have seen her blush, and, indeed, he had probably not even heard what she had said.

Presently, feeling less shaken, she returned to her room and climbed back into bed, where she lay awake for a while, concentrating on the mystery of 'Mr Childers', which was more intriguing and much less disturbing than thinking about Mr Hartwell.

Surely she had not been mistaken in her recognition of the man? That stout figure, the sharply-projecting nose, which always reminded her of a duck's bill, the full, sulky, down-turning mouth . . . Even the mention of Yorkshire was significant, for a few years ago he had been a wool-merchant there, and even the curt bow and the lack of any word of acknowledgment were typical of his boorish attitude towards the common courtesies of

Society . . . But why was he here, discussing business with Mr Hartwell in the middle of the night?

It was not difficult to guess a reason, in view of what Mr Bell had said about his need of money, and it would be an embarrassment, something to be hidden by darkness, for him to have to resort to seeking financial help from such as 'Mr Childers'.

Having found a satisfactory explanation to the whole business, Caroline composed herself to sleep, dreamed most disturbingly, and woke early to a near-repeat performance of the morning of Mr Hartwell's last return from his travels, for when she looked from her window, she again saw him in the garden, and again she went downstairs to seek him out, and came upon him in much the same place as before.

'Good morning, Caroline,' he said soberly, looking at her in a somewhat wary fashion. 'I trust that your early appearance doesn't mean that you were unable to sleep after last night's adventure?'

'No, not at all, thank you. I usually wake quite early. I came down because I wish to say something to you privately.'

'Yes?' He seemed to tense, as if expecting that whatever she had to say would be unpleasant. The morning was a little misty, and a heavy dew had made the seat too wet to sit on, so instead they paced slowly along the garden path in silence, while Caroline collected her thoughts.

'Mr Hartwell,' she began.

He sighed. 'I thought for one glorious moment last night that I heard you address me less formally.' Fortunately, he did not look at her, and so presumably missed seeing her heightened colour.

'Mr Hartwell,' she repeated firmly, 'I know that your business affairs are nothing to do with me, and no doubt you would resent any intrusion into them on my part, but

I do feel that I must say one thing. If you need to borrow money, pray approach my father. You wouldn't find him a difficult or unreasonable man to deal with.' She waited with some nervousness for the inevitable cold set-down which her presumption might almost be admitted to have merited.

Mr Hartwell stopped in his tracks and stared at her in patent astonishment. 'What makes you think I need to borrow money?' he asked mildly.

'Your "Mr Childers" left Yorkshire for London some years ago,' Caroline replied obliquely. 'He's a very shrewd and clever man, and a notably honest banker, but he does charge a high rate of interest!'

'Ah, so you did recognise him. He thought you might!'

'It would be difficult not to recognise Mr Rothschild. He has very distinctive features, and I have met him several times.'

'Oh, Caroline! What a remarkable female you are!' Mr Hartwell exclaimed, sounding positively joyful. 'You and I must marry, you know, for we'd be a formidable partnership! You think your father would lend at a lower rate because of the family connection, perhaps?'

'I should think so.' Caroline tried to keep her voice level and cool, and concentrated very hard on ignoring his reference to—no, she must even think of the word! 'I've nothing against Mr Rothschild, you understand —he has an excellent reputation—but he's a banker, and has to make a profit for his customers.'

'But why do you think I need to borrow? May not a man discuss business with a banker for any other reason?'

'In secret, in the middle of the night?'

Mr Hartwell was silent, and appeared to be considering something very carefully. At length, he said quietly, 'Caroline, I'm about to tell you something which could endanger many lives, and even bring about the defeat of this country by Bonaparte if it even got out, but I shall tell you so that you may see how much I trust and respect you.'

She could only look at him in amazement, and wonder if she had run mad—surely he could not really have said that?

'Nathan Rothschild is, indeed, a banker, and so are his father and his five brothers, but only Nathan is in England. The rest of the family is in Europe, and they have many connections—business connections, in most of the continental capitals.'

He paused, and looked at Caroline, who replied 'Yes,' as he seemed to expect an answer.

'Have you ever thought about armies?' he continued, apparently on a totally different tack. 'They have to be fed, clothed, equipped, and paid. Thousands of men, moving about all over the place, often in hostile territory. The French haven't managed to solve the problems that are entailed, and their armies take what they need from the country through which they pass. The result is that they leave a desert, a countryside stripped of everything, and the populace are, naturally, left destitute and filled with hate.'

'Yes,' Caroline said again as he had once more paused and looked at her questioningly. Then, as he still waited, she added, 'It would take a great deal of organising to do otherwise. I mean—either the army would have to have everything sent to them from their own country, or they would have to buy what they needed, and pay for it in acceptable money—in gold, presumably.'

Mr Hartwell smiled at her with every appearance of affection. 'My estimable Caroline! Indeed, it does take organisation! Men must travel about the country, ordering quantities of boots and biscuits, ropes and rifles, stockings and shirts, and other men must find wagons to carry them to the ships, which yet other men must find to transport it all. But immediate needs—fresh food and transport animals, for instance—must be bought on the spot, and that needs cash in hand—gold, as you so shrewdly observe! Now, if you were going, say, to Edinburgh, and were sure to need a quantity of gold when you arrived there, how would you take it? In your reticule?'

'Indeed not, for it might be stolen, and it would be very heavy. I should go to a banker who had a connection in Edinburgh . . .' She broke off, met Mr Hartwell's now amused and approving gaze, and could not help but smile in reply.

'Oh, I see!' she said. 'Yes, of course! You would have to meet secretly to arrange that. How very fortunate that Mr—er—Childers has so many relations!'

'Why, Robert!' called Julia's voice from the terrace, fortunately some distance from where they were standing. 'How very obliging of you to return for my dinner! I had quite determined last evening that you had forgot about it!'

'How could I possibly forget something so important as my sister's first dinner-party in her own home?' Mr Hartwell replied in his usual slightly sardonic tone. 'Here I am, primed for genteel conversation, and at your service. What do you mean to give us to eat?'

'I told you I should leave that to Cook,' Julia replied airily. 'I'm sure she knows what will be best, and the evening will be a great success.'

Despite her confidence in Cook, Julia made frequent mention during the morning of the weight of responsibility resting on her as hostess, and decided to lie down in the afternoon in order to be quite rested when her guests arrived, so Caroline took the opportunity to go out walking with Horatio, in order to think over her conversation with Mr Hartwell.

She was chiefly concerned with sorting out exactly what was involved in the secret of such importance that he had confided to her, or, rather, had left her to work out for herself, and she concluded that he had meant that his journeys about the country were concerned with obtaining supplies for the army—presumably the one in Portugal as there was no other British force at present on foreign soil. (Like most British people, she forgot about the garrisons in her country's many overseas possessions.) She also concluded that Mr Hartwell's meeting with Mr Rothschild was to do with the transfer of credit to the same destination.

Eventually, finding herself by a watercourse which she thought to be the Cornmill stream in one of its higher reaches, she sat down on a conveniently low branch on the bank, and gazed unseeingly at the water, while Horatio happily investigated the activities of water-rats and suchlike, much to their annoyance, with quivering nose and wagging tail.

Rather unwillingly, she allowed herself to think about Mr Hartwell's jocular reference to marriage. Surely it was only a joke? She felt so very uncertain now about everything concerning him, for her feelings were in a state of utter confusion. She was still not at all sure that she could ever have any liking for him, and yet he had such a disturbing effect on her. Was he overbearing, or was he just genuinely concerned about Julia's welfare? Was he really arrogant and disagreeable, or had she perhaps mistaken his character from the first?

Why, if she disliked him, had she put herself to the embarrassment of suggesting that he should ask her father to lend him money? And surely, if he were really arrogant, he would have been mortally offended at her interference? What had he actually meant by saying that she should marry him? Surely she could not wish it to be anything but a joke, but why should her growing belief that the remark had no serious meaning leave her feeling so depressed?

'Oh, Horatio! What am I to do?' she asked. 'What on earth is the matter with me? I've never felt so wretched and confused in all my life!'

Horatio removed his head from a particularly delectable hole in the bank and looked at her enquiringly, then took a step or two towards her and made a rumbling remark which sounded like a question.

'Now I come to think of it, he didn't actually say that he had no need of money,' she continued, 'and Mr Bell seemed very sure . . . I suppose all that he said could be true, and yet he could still be looking for a rich wife as well. I just don't understand him, Horatio. He makes no effort to please me most of the time, as—say—Captain Marsh does, and yet he speaks to me at other times as if there were some sort of understanding between us, and there isn't!'

At that moment, Horatio, who had resumed his investigations, came nose to nose with a rabbit, which, being the first to recover, took off at speed downstream. Horatio gave an excited yip and set off after it, but miscalculated and fell into the stream with a spectacular splash. Caroline leapt to her feet in alarm and went to his rescue, but the dog broke surface, swam to the bank, and scrambled out without any particular difficulty. Caroline arrived on the spot only in time to be showered comprehensively with water and duckweed as he shook himself energetically, grumbling loudly as he did so.

For some unknown reason, the incident raised Caroline's spirits as much as it dampened her skirts, and she resumed her walk in a better humour, resolving not to brood over Mr Hartwell any more, but to wait and see what happened.

Julia proved to be right in trusting to Cook's professional expertise, for the dinner was well chosen, perfectly cooked and beautifully presented, and Julia herself, very much in looks and becomingly gowned in her new silk, queened it over her guests most enjoyably, with Major Bridges, obviously completely captivated, by her side. Caroline, however, felt that the evening's success was not entirely unalloyed.

To begin with, she was paired with Captain Marsh, whose attentions were far too pressing for comfort, for he completely ignored Mrs Calvert on his other side and tried to monopolise her attention all through dinner, so that she was unable to converse with John Cressing on her other side, and so put the whole table out.

To make matters worse, she was seated directly opposite to Mr Hartwell and Miss Enstone, for Julia had taken the head of the table herself and put the Rector at the foot, as if to make it plain that this was her party, and her brother was no more than one of the guests. The result of this arrangement was that Caroline felt herself to be under the scrutiny of Miss Enstone's sharp little eyes all the time, which made her even more self-conscious about Captain Marsh's behaviour, and quite unable to look across the table for fear of meeting those watchful eyes, or, even worse, finding that Mr Hartwell was also observing her, which she felt quite sure he was, and no doubt with some amusement, for she had an unpleasant feeling that she was not coping at all well with the situation.

The meal eventually ended, and the ladies followed Julia to the parlour, leaving the gentlemen to their port, cigars, and whatever else they found to occupy themselves with after the withdrawal of the female half of the party. Caroline had often wondered, but had long ago decided that it was probably business talk or doubtful stories. Certainly the conversation over coffee in the parlour was not particularly exciting, but it gave her a respite from the pressures she had endured during dinner, and was consequently most welcome.

The gentlemen, however, did not linger for long in the dismal dining-room, and soon came to the parlour, disturbing Horatio again when he had barely got off to sleep after the female incursion. Captain Marsh made an immediate bee-line for Caroline, followed closely by Mr Hartwell, who, with a wicked gleam in his eye, took the seat beside her on her sofa while Captain Marsh was still doing the polite over enquiring if she wished for more coffee or tea, so that the Captain was forced to be content with drawing up a chair at a right angle to her. But he did succeed in engaging her in conversation again, for Mr Hartwell said very little, only listening with apparent close attention and throwing in a comment or a remark when the Captain's flow of small-talk seemed likely to dry up.

'The evening is fine, and there's no wind—would you perhaps care to take a turn on the terrace?' the Captain enquired in a determined fashion when it had become obvious that Mr Hartwell had no intention of making a tactful withdrawal.

'Midges,' that gentleman remarked *sotto voce*, but not sufficiently so for Captain Marsh to be unable to hear him.

'Oh, yes!' Caroline replied to the Captain. 'I'm afraid Mr Hartwell is quite right—the midges do bite quite dreadfully on these mild evenings!'

'Caro, dearest!' Julia called across the room. 'Will you not play for us? Have you your music to hand?'

'Well, I did bring it down,' she admitted, 'but I seem to have left it in the dining-room.'

'I'll fetch it!' Captain Marsh sprang to his feet and was gone before she could protest or Julia instruct a footman to go on the errand.

'If you're not careful,' Mr Hartwell murmured softly, 'that young man will be making you a proposal, and you'll be put to the embarrassment of refusing him! You really must be more discouraging!'

'Why are you so sure I would refuse him?' Caroline enquired, piqued by his apparent bland assurance.

'Oh, it wouldn't do: you might just as well marry Horatio. Blind adoration would become excessively boring in no time at all! Besides, you know very well that you'd do better to marry me!'

'I know nothing of the sort!' she replied a little breathlessly, wondering if the odd flutter in her throat was hope or fear. 'In any case, I'm sure he's only being well-mannered to a comparative newcomer. Why, he's only met me three or four times!'

'*"Whoever loved who loved not at first sight?"*' he quoted. 'Shakespeare.'

'Marlowe,' Caroline corrected firmly, finding some pleasure in putting him both right and down.

'True,' he replied, unruffled. 'Not a customary author for study by young ladies—I rejoice to find you so well read! Ah, here comes your young admirer with your music. I'll open the pianoforte for you.' He rose to his feet in a leisurely fashion, prepared the instrument for Caroline's performance, and neatly ended the operation in the right place for turning the pages of her music, completely cutting out Captain Marsh, who was forced to confine his support to listening with rapt attention while Caroline played two or three of her favourite pieces.

She was not a brilliant musician, but somewhat better than the average young lady, and her efforts were rewarded by applause and murmurs of appreciation, and even a couple of cries of 'Encore!', but she smilingly declined, suggesting that someone else might care to play or sing, and those present who were able and willing duly took their turn at providing entertainment until supper was served.

When she rose from the pianoforte, Caroline took care to move more towards the centre of the gathering and took a seat beside Lucinda, which happened to fall vacant because Colonel Long, who had been occupying it, had volunteered to sing, and, as Lucinda followed him and he took her vacated seat and remained in it, Captain Marsh was successfully but not too obviously staved off for the rest of the evening.

He did make an effort, as he was bidding her good night when the party broke up, to establish that there was some sort of understanding between them by pressing her hand in a meaningful fashion, and saying very earnestly, 'I hope I shall have the pleasure of being in your company again very soon.' To which Caroline, extracting her hand in as natural a fashion as she could contrive, replied vaguely, 'Oh, I am sure we shall run into one another somewhere or other before long.'

To judge by his rather crestfallen expression, Captain Marsh interpreted this lukewarm response correctly, and directed an appealing look straight into her eyes, but, although she did not wish to hurt his feelings, she steeled herself to turn away with a laughing reply to some remark of the Rector's, knowing that it would be more unkind in the long run to give the Captain any encouragement. She was quite certain that she had no wish to become Mrs Captain Marsh, adding to herself that, although Mr Hartwell might be right in that respect, he had no business to flatter himself that she would prefer to marry him, even if he had been serious in suggesting such an eventuality, which she doubted.

That, she decided later when she was in bed, was the trouble. Surely a man who spoke so lightly about marriage could not be giving it any serious consideration? It was just one of his peculiar remarks which might or might not be intended as jokes. Or was it perhaps part of a campaign to inveigle her into marriage for the sake of the not inconsiderable settlement he would expect her father to provide for his elder daughter, as Mr Bell had hinted—nay, more than hinted!

She reconsidered her conversation with him in the garden that morning, and reminded herself that, to the best of her recollection, he had not denied that he was in need of money, although the borrowing of it had not been the object of his meeting with Mr Rothschild.

At this point her thoughts were interrupted by a tapping at her bedroom door, which heralded the arrival of Julia, looking a little like Lady Macbeth in her nightrobe with a candle and a tragical expression.

'Oh, Caro! You're not asleep, are you? Oh, good! I do need your advice!'

She perched on the edge on Caroline's bed, spilling a little candlegrease on the sheet in the process, and went on, 'I really don't know what to do! I don't know if you've noticed, but dear Major Bridges has been—well—most attentive to me lately, and this evening he—he asked me if—if he dared hope . . . !'

She gazed at Caroline with eyes as big as twopenny pieces, and Caroline replied, as she thought was expected, 'Why, that's splendid!'

'Yes, it is rather,' Julia replied with some satisfaction, but quickly resumed her tragical aspect. 'But what should I do? Would it be a fearful betrayal of dearest Charles if I—well—gave encouragement to Another? I mean—it's not as if Robert would ever give his consent to my marrying dearest Charles, and dearest James —Major Bridges told me his name is James—is it not a pleasant name?—and dearest James is very eligible, and so very handsome!'

'Do you love him?' Caroline enquired, thinking that, unless she brought matters to a head, Julia might well go on burbling all night.

'Well, yes, I do!'

'Are you quite sure?' Caroline insisted. 'If I were you, I should give myself more time to think it over, for it's a mistake to rush too quickly into an engagement. What if you find, after a few weeks, that you are not happy with the thought of marriage to Major Bridges after all?'

'Oh, I'm sure I shall be perfectly happy!' Julia assured her rapturously. 'If not, I should simply break the engagement!'

'Better not to have entered into it in the first place!' Caroline said sharply. 'A young lady who breaks an engagement gains an unpleasant reputation as a jilt! If you really value my advice, Julia, think very carefully, and then, if you are quite certain, marry him. If he asks you. Good night!'

CHAPTER
ELEVEN

THIS DID not, of course, end the conversation, for Julia had to go on for another half-hour or so explaining how she had been forced to the conclusion that she had been mistaken about her feelings for dearest Charles, but, with that experience to build on, was now quite sure that her feelings for dearest James were of a truly enduring nature, and so on and so forth, but she did eventually come to a conclusion, and trotted off happily after kissing Caroline most affectionately and thanking her for her advice.

By then, Caroline was too sleepy to think any further about her own problems, and deferred them until the morning, when they seemed to have receded a little, for Mr Hartwell was preoccupied at breakfast, and went out immediately after, presumably to pursue the preparations for his Harvest Supper.

Julia, of course, was recovering from the exertions of the previous evening, so Caroline, despite a cloudy sky, set out to walk into town with Horatio, partly for exercise, and partly to match a skein of embroidery silk for her needlework.

She chose to take the route of her first walk in the valley, but in reverse, so that she approached the town by way of the Cornmill stream path and the orchard, whose gate was no longer locked now that the fruit was all picked, and so through the churchyard, where she paused to look at the broken stumps of wall and arch protruding from the truncated east end of the church.

The building had an oddly unfinished look about it, and she wondered why, in the two and a half centuries since the Dissolution of the Abbey, the parish had not managed to make a tidier job of the east end, for surely it would be possible to remove the broken stumps and put in a better window than that ugly rectangular thing which quite spoiled the look of the interior?

Horatio, snuffling about among the gravestones, drew her attention with a sharp yip, and she saw that he was standing by a small door at the northern side of the east wall, looking over his shoulder at her as if to call her to come and look at something. She obligingly joined him, and found that the door stood ajar, and Horatio seemed to think that there was something of interest within.

She peered inside, and saw that the door opened, as she expected, into the north aisle of the church, just beside the Sanctuary, and, after a moment's hesitation, she told Horatio to 'stay', and went inside, welcoming the opportunity to have another look round by herself, without giving anyone the inconvenience of accompanying her or letting her in.

The interior was shadowy and dimly-lit on this overcast day. 'Crepuscular' thought Caroline with relish, for she liked unusual words. She knelt to pray more from habit and a sense of duty than immediate inclination, but found that the act of putting into words her concern for Julia and her personal perplexities seemed to set them in a better perspective, and she rose from her knees in a state of mind much nearer to her natural tranquillity, and wandered on round the church, pausing to look at whatever caught her eye, until at length she reached the little door in the corner which gave access to the tower stairs. It was open.

Remembering Lord Cressing's warning about the dangers of bell-towers, she hesitated, wondering what to do. The fact that it, and the door by which she had entered the church, were both open, when normally they were kept closed and locked, was puzzling, but none of her business. On the other hand, if she had wandered into the building on finding the outer door open, might not a child do the same, and then go on to climb the stairs out of curiosity, and perhaps meet with some dreadful accident? Perhaps she should do something about it . . .

Then again, if someone was working in the tower, perhaps repairing a bell-rope, or whatever one had to do to keep bells happy, she would feel very foolish if she raised the alarm at the Rectory and disturbed the folk there for no good reason . . .

Being an honest person, she had to admit to herself that she was curious about why the doors were open, and would like to see the inside of the tower again, for her earlier visit had been concerned with going to the top, and she had not had an opportunity to look at the odd inscriptions on the walls, or the peal-boards in the ringing-chamber. Perhaps whoever was up there would allow her to look about, and tell her more about the tower and the bells.

By the time she had convinced herself that these were all perfectly good reasons for climbing the stairs, she was already part of the way up, so she continued, pausing from time to time to decipher the names of bygone ringers cut into the wall of the stairs, or to peer out of the little apertures which lit her way, catching odd glimpses through them which amused or intrigued her—an odd carved face on one of the projections of the west front, a pigeon sitting on its nest on a ledge, and an oblique view of the Rectory garden, where a stout black and white cat gambolled after a windblown leaf. Eventually she reached the three high steps to the door which opened on the clerestory, but prudently did not try to open it.

The stairs ceased, and gave way to the stone-flagged short passage to the ringing-chamber, and then she heard voices, and paused, not sure whether to go on and risk the embarrassment of being lectured for trespassing, or to turn back before she was discovered. She was aware now that the reasons for coming up here which had seemed good enough at the foot of the stairs now seemed but a thin cover for sheer curiosity, and there was something about the quiet murmur from behind the closed door at the end of the passage which gave her the impression that the conversation was private.

She turned, and had taken a couple of steps back the way she had come, when one of the voices said more loudly, 'But I assure you that there's no possible risk to you or your friends!' in the unmistakable tones of Mr Hartwell.

Startled, she turned again, but caught her foot on the edge of an unevenly set stone and pitched sideways against the wall, dropping her reticule. Its soft leather made no sound as it landed on the floor, but a handful of coins fell out of it and tinkled on the stone flags.

'What was that?' she heard, and the ringing-chamber door was flung open, lighting the passage where she was already stooping to pick up the coins.

'What on earth . . . ? Why, Caroline! What brings you here?' Mr Hartwell asked sharply, coming towards her. A tall, broad figure followed him, silhouetted against the light and unrecognisable to her, yet appearing so large and menacing that she shrank back, catching her breath in a moment of panic.

'What are you doing here?' he asked again, his voice pleasant, but with an underlying sharpness that sounded a warning to her to mind what she said.

'The—the door was open,' she stammered. 'I wondered if someone was up here, or if it had been left open by mistake. Lord Cressing told me that it's kept locked because the tower can be dangerous.'

'It can that!' confirmed the other man in a deep, rough voice which had a familiar but unplaceable ring to it. The words sounded to Caroline rather like a threat, and she shivered slightly, wondering what her foolish curiosity had led her into.

'Did you trip over? The stones are uneven, I'm afraid,' Mr Hartwell said, bending to pick up her reticule and handing it back to her. 'You'd better come into the ringing-chamber,' and he put one hand on her arm and gently propelled her through the doorway. The tall man retreated before her, and once they were in the room, with the light falling on him instead of exaggerating his size from behind, the unknown ceased to be so.

'Why, it's . . . !' she began to exclaim, then realised that she did not know his name.

'Will Plomer,' Mr Hartwell supplied. 'You probably recall him from your encounter in the Forest when we went riding.'

'Mr Plomer,' Caroline gave him a courteous nod.

'Miss Barnes,' he responded, with a similar nod. 'Here yer finds me at home, so ter speak.'

'Will is Captain of the Tower,' Mr Hartwell put in, 'and our local blacksmith, of course. A very important figure in a rural community.'

'Ar. I has the magic o' the cold iron!' he affirmed with apparent solemnity, and Caroline, with an apprehensive internal tremor of something like superstition, wondered if he were really as serious as he sounded.

'And do you ring bells too, then?' she asked Mr Hartwell with an assumption of lightness and interest, for she still had an uneasy feeling that she had come upon something which these two men did not wish her to know, some secret, possibly with an element of danger. For there was a watchfulness about both of them, and a tendency to avoid looking at each other which was more sinister, she felt, than any number of significant exchanged glances.

'Occasionally, if the ringers are a man short,' he

replied easily. 'Why do you say "too"? Do you know another ringer hereabouts, then?'

'Yes. Lord Cressing and Lady Lucinda brought me up here on Monday, while we were looking round the church.'

For some reason, this statement seemed to ease the tension a little. Will Plomer said lightly, 'And yer thought yer'd have another look while th' opportunity offered, I s'pose,' and turned away to loop up a bell-rope which had been left hanging at its full length, while Mr Hartwell leaned back against the doorpost.

'Did you go to the top?' he asked.

'Yes. There is a very fine view.'

'Indeed. Perhaps you'd care to go up again, as you're here. You're half-way up already, so you may as well.'

'Oh, I should like that very much, if it's not too much trouble!' Caroline hesitated and glanced at Will Plomer. 'Perhaps you're busy, though . . . ?'

'No. We've finished our business, I think.' Mr Hartwell also glanced at the silent blacksmith. 'Is there anything else, Will, or are you satisfied?'

'Ay. Yer word's good enough fer me,' Mr Plomer said. 'Red, yer said, and red it shall be!'

Caroline looked at him with a puzzled frown, wondering why a common labourer should speak to a gentleman in such an easy, man-to-man fashion, and she recalled that she had wondered much the same about Mr Warrener. Then she realised what the two had in common. Neither was, in fact, a labourer at all, but a skilled craftsman with a secure place in the world, and as good, in his own way, as any man in England—even, she thought with a flash of humorous recollection, a Freeman of the City of London!

'Then, with your permission . . . ?' Mr Hartwell said, and Caroline opened her lips to say 'By all means,' but realised just in time that he was still talking to the

Captain of the Tower, who, of course, had every right to give or withhold permission to go among the bells, and it was Mr Plomer who said the words, with a surprisingly graceful gesture of invitation towards the steep wooden steps.

Mr Hartwell nodded in reply, turned and climbed the steps to open the trapdoor at the top. Caroline, with only a momentary hesitation, put her shawl and reticule on the table, then followed him.

The clock-chamber was in darkness, but Mr Hartwell did not open the panel by the clock-face. Instead, he put his hands on her shoulders and guided her towards the steps which led upwards through the bell-chamber. It was an odd sensation, to be in complete darkness—a darkness which seemed to vibrate with the sonorous ticking of the clock—with another person standing so close behind her that she could almost feel him breathing, and yet she could not see him at all, or even the hands which gripped her shoulders. For a moment, she had a horrible feeling that those hands might slip inwards and upwards to close about her neck, and . . . She gave herself a mental shake, thinking that she was fast becoming a fanciful imbecile who saw menace in everything!

The hands pushed her gently forwards, and a quiet voice said, 'The first step is just before your feet. Take your time.' She found it, and began to ascend, her companion waiting patiently until she was sure of her footing on each successive step, his hands on her shoulders making her feel safe from falling among the bells, yet still nervous about their owner.

As they mounted the steps and her head rose above the floor of the bell-chamber, the light coming in through the louvres enabled her to see fairly well, but Mr Hartwell's hands remained on her shoulders, steadying her.

'I assume you've made the acquaintance of our fine brazen voices?' he said. 'Can you see them now?'

She paused to look over the wooden rail at her side, and saw the silent shapes of the bells, hanging there, waiting for their masters to come and release their voices.

'Faith, Hope and Charity,' she whispered. 'James and John. Raphael, Michael and Gabriel.'

There was a stirring in the shadows, half-heard, half-felt, and one of the bells spoke in the softest of whispers.

'Oh!' she exclaimed. 'Did they reply?'

'In a way,' said a subdued voice in her ear. 'I touched one with my foot, but that wouldn't necessarily cause it to greet you! Bells are strange creatures!'

'So are you!' Caroline thought, but she kept the observation to herself, and went on up the steps.

In a few moments they had reached the top. Mr Hartwell stretched past her to open the door on to the roof, and they stepped out into a brisk breeze which set the clouds racing, and allowed fitful gleams of sunshine to break through and touch the weathercock's gilded wings. Caroline found that the wind struck chill through her light muslin frock, and regretted leaving her shawl down below. She moved as quickly as caution allowed round to the north side of the tower, which was sheltered by the pyramidal roof rising in the middle. He followed her, silently took off his coat and draped it round her shoulders, then stood close beside and a little behind her as she leaned against the parapet.

'Thank you,' she said, then, at a loss for some more intelligent remark, added brightly, 'the army camp appears very busy.'

'Like an ant-heap,' he agreed. 'Cressing brought you up here, did he? Did you think the view worth the climb?'

'Oh, yes! Well worth it! One can see quite a distance.'

'You can see further from the ridge above the house.'

'Yes. I remarked on that to Lord Cressing. He said that . . .' She broke off, recalling the subject of the rest of her conversation with Lord Cressing.

'That what?' Mr Hartwell prompted.

'Oh, something about it being unfortunate that the camp is overlooked from so many points of vantage. He said that there was some trouble here last year about a French spy.'

'Yes. I wasn't involved in the matter, being away at the time, but I heard about it afterwards.'

'What became of him?'

'Who—the spy? Cressing sent him back to France, I understand.'

'How odd! Why did he do that?'

'The fellow's usefulness to his master was ended with his unmasking, and he was well liked by those who knew him. No one wished to pursue him to the grave, whatever he'd done.'

'Would he have been . . . ? I mean, if he'd been arrested and brought to trial?'

'Hanged.'

'Oh!' Caroline digested this, and felt that Lord Cressing's action had been right. 'What puzzles me,' she said, 'is how a spy could send information to France. Did he use pigeons, do you suppose?'

'Possibly, but it's not difficult to send a letter to France, you know. There are people who have frequent dealings with the French, despite the war. Apart from Mr Rothschild, of course. I'd not wish to suggest that he is up to anything unpatriotirc!'

'But who . . .? Oh, you mean the smug—!' Caroline broke off so sharply in the middle of the word that she felt her lower jaw lock rigidly and cause her chin to tremble for a moment before she could close her mouth, and a number of thoughts ran through her head,

apparently unconnected, yet forming a picture . . .
Smugglers—Will Plomer—an odd scrap of conversation
with Julia—the ponies and the waiting man in the
Forest—Mr Hartwell's confidential conversation in the
ringing-chamber with the same man, and the uneasy
atmosphere when they had found her outside the
door . . .

'Next time, I should keep the whole word to yourself!'
Mr Hartwell said drily. 'The nighthawks risk their lives
in what they do, and they've a short and unpleasant way
with anyone who talks too freely about them—and an
even shorter and nastier way with someone they think
may be spying on them. They'd hardly help Bonaparte
to conquer England, would they? It would ruin their
trade!'

Caroline ignored the jocular tone of his last two
sentences, and said indignantly, 'Spying? Surely you
don't imagine I was spying on anyone when I came up
the tower. Why, I didn't even know who was there, or,
indeed, if anyone was!' She turned to face Mr Hartwell
as she spoke, and met his cool, considering gaze with an
angry glare. 'I'm not in the habit of spying on anyone!'

'Oh, I believe you!' His lips twitched, and an amused
glint appeared in his eyes. 'I think you're just cursed with
a little more than the average feminine curiosity and
intelligence. Be careful, that's all! Let the latter govern
the former and keep it in cheek. Remember what curiosity did to the cat, and don't turn yours in the direction
of Will Plomer and his associates! A female can easily
meet with an accident, deserved or not.'

'An accident?'

'Consider how easily I could seize you so . . .' He
made a sudden grab, and she found herself held tightly in
his arms, crushed against his body. After the first moment of shock, she tried to struggle, but he had her arms
pinned at her sides, and her attempts to kick him were

ineffective, despite her walking-boots, for he was wearing hessians.

'. . . and, having seized you, I could quite easily force you back into an embrasure and tip you over, then run down to the ground in a great state of shocked horror, with a fine tale of how you leant over too far, and fell before I could save you! Don't worry,' he added as she gasped, then drew breath to scream. 'I've no intention of doing it, but you see how easy it would be!'

He was looking straight into her face from a distance of mere inches, and their eyes met and locked for a moment. She saw the serious warning behind his cool gaze, and then, suddenly, his eyes seemed almost to change colour, and she read in them something which she did not comprehend, something which made her heart flutter and her legs tremble so much that she was glad to cling to him for a moment until her body returned to normal. Then he released her and moved away a little.

'I'm sorry. I meant to frighten you, but only enough to make you understand,' he said mildly. 'It was only a warning. Do be careful where your curious nature takes you, that's all. I've no wish to carry your accidentally-killed body home to your parents!'

'I take your point,' Caroline replied breathlessly. 'Perhaps you should give Julia a similar warning—it was she who told me about Will Plomer's activities.'

'No—in fact, it was I, after she had hinted very broadly about his unofficial capacity. I should have attached a warning to the information then, but I assumed you knew of the dangers. Don't worry about Plomer at the moment, though—I think he's gathered that you have no ill-will towards him, and if he says anything to me, I'll tell him you're to be trusted.'

'Thank you!' Caroline replied tartly, and was stung to add, 'I thought, from your earlier remarks, that you thought otherwise!'

Mr Hartwell's unperturbed smile appeared, and he said, 'No—I have no doubts about your trustworthiness. I'd not have told you about my nocturnal visitor, or my official activities, if I had. I just fear that your curiosity might lead you into deep waters, that's all.'

He pulled a watch from his waistcoat pocket and apparently found that it agreed with the sounds of chiming bells which had suddenly broken out below and round about them, for, as soon as the sound had moderated sufficiently, he said, 'D'you mind if we go down now? I've more business to see to this morning, and time is slipping by.'

'Certainly,' Caroline replied, and added civilly, 'thank you for bringing me up here.'

'My pleasure,' he assured her with equal civility, and took her down to the ringing-chamber again, this time going backwards before her and holding her hands to guide and steady her. He let her negotiate the last ladder by herself while he closed the trapdoor, for Mr Plomer stood at the foot of the steps and presumably would catch her if she fell.

'Your bells are very fine,' she said politely to the Captain. 'I'd never seen a peal of bells before, until Lord Cressing took me up, and I'd no idea they were so large!'

'A ring,' he corrected her quite kindly. 'A peal is what yer rings on 'em. Yes, we've a ring to be proud of here, and I'm pleased yer thinks well on 'em. Not many leddies appreciates bell music!'

'Has Mrs Willoughby been complaining again?' enquired Mr Hartwell, retrieving his coat from Caroline and inserting himself into it with practised ease, despite its excellent fit.

'Ar. Says th' noise sends her lapdog inter high stericks!' Mr Plomer said grimly. 'I told her, bells was here afore lapdogs, but she'm an 'ooman as must be complaining about summat and she still went on, so I telled her that them as don't like bells don't like brandy neether, and that shut her good, that did!' He gave a very sinister-sounding chuckle and winked at Caroline, who deduced from this that he at least thought her trustworthy enough to share a joke. Nevertheless, she decided, it would be best to heed Mr Hartwell's warning, and not appear too curious about the nighthawk's exploits.

'We'll be off, then,' Mr Hartwell said briskly, opening the door and holding it for Caroline to pass through before him.

'Ar. I've a few things to see arter afore I goes to me forge,' Mr Plomer said vaguely. 'Abaht yer passel—I'll see it safe ter yer door, never fear.'

'Thank you. Good day to you.' Mr Hartwell hurried Caroline out, barely giving her time for a polite 'Good morning' to Mr Plomer, and led the way down the uneven winding stairs rather too quickly for comfort, so she followed at a slower and safer pace, and found him waiting a trifle impatiently at the bottom.

'I can find my way out,' she said pointedly.

'Yes—that reminds me—how did you get in?'

'The little door at the other end of the aisle was open.'

'Was it? I thought I latched it!'

'Horatio drew my attention to it. It was standing ajar.'

'Oh, I expect he caught my scent. The latch is old, and perhaps not very secure. I must tell Briggs that it needs replacing.'

The small door was still standing ajar when they reached it, and Mr Hartwell closed and latched it firmly behind them, but after a moment it creaked itself ajar again, much to Caroline's relief, for it confirmed what she had said and, she felt, cleared her of any suspicion of going about trying doors to see if they were open.

She looked about for Horatio, wondering if he had become tired of waiting and had taken himself off. She felt a momentary panic for fear he might be lost, but was relieved to see him quite close, *vis-à-vis* with Mr Briggs, the sexton, who was sitting on a tomb contemplating a heap of small furry corpses on a gravestone between him and the dog.

'Regular little mouser, this yin!' he announced, creaking to his feet as Caroline and Mr Hartwell approached. 'He's catched all these in the long grass round the tombs in jest a few minutes! Dunno what Fred'll say, mind! He reckons all churchyard meeces is his perky sites, him being th' Rectory cat.'

'I'm sure he can spare a few for a visitor—they must be quite plentiful,' Mr Hartwell said absently, tugging out his watch again. 'You'll forgive me, Cousin Caroline, if I abandon you to Horatio's escort? I must go. I'm late already.'

'I'm sorry I've delayed . . .' Caroline began, but he shook his head, and said, 'Don't worry about that! I've much enjoyed our conversation—in a manner of speaking, that is! Mind how you go!' And with this equivocal statement, smiled enigmatically and strode off towards the town.

'Will yer be wanting the bodies?' Mr Briggs asked in a gloomy tone. Caroline started, thinking he was speaking to her, but discovered that the question had been addressed to Horatio, who answered by turning his back on his victims and making a few prancing movements of a hopeful nature in the direction of home.

Caroline bade Mr Briggs 'Good day', and followed the dog, thinking about the strange scene on the top of the church tower. She wondered if Mr Hartwell's warning had been only against prying into the smugglers' activities, for, if so, it had been a little overdone, surely? There had been no need to give her such a fright in order to remind her of something which she already knew quite well! Besides, most people referred to smuggling without much concealment, apart from some obliqueness of speech and various nods and winks, for almost everyone bought from smugglers, even in the City, and everyone knew that it was unwise to show much interest in the smugglers themselves, or their way of business, for fear of arousing their instincts of self-preservation. Perhaps he had been hinting at danger to herself more from prying into his own affairs, and she wondered about the reason he had given for Mr Rothschild's visit. It had sounded convincing at the time, but had it perhaps been a little too glib? She could accept that what he had said about organising the supply of *matériel* and money to an army overseas was perfectly true—someone had to see to it—but he had not actually said that he was one of the men who did it. Perhaps he had lied by implication? Perhaps his meeting with Mr Rothschild had been about that, or maybe it had been, as she had at first assumed, about borrowing money for himself, or perhaps it had some more sinister purpose . . .

'Oh dear, Horatio! I don't know what to believe any more!' she said to the dog, who was ranging to and fro across the path in front of her. 'I'm sure he was asking Mr Plomer to bring him something which was more risky than brandy or silk, and what could be red? I don't wish to think him a villain, or even just a liar, but I don't know—I just don't know what to think!'

Horatio paused to give her a look and a brief tail-wag in passing as an expression of sympathy, but had nothing further to offer, being engaged in reading the local news with his nose, and she went slowly on her way, still thinking in a confused fashion about Mr Hartwell and his odd behaviour.

Presently it dawned on her that a few minutes' rest would not come amiss, and she looked about her for somewhere to sit. There was a fallen tree-trunk a little further along, between the path and the stream, and she sat down on it and idly watched Horatio casting about, following his nose. He went back a little along the way they had come, then disappeared under a bush on the river-bank.

As she turned to see where he had gone, Caroline glanced back along the path, and saw someone striding along towards her. He was still a long way off, but she had little difficulty in recognising him, for it was unusual for a man to be so tall and so thick-set about the shoulders. It was Mr Plomer!

Her first reaction was to get up and hurry off as fast as she could, but at the rate he was walking he would soon overtake her long before she reached home. Then she realised that she was wearing green, and the bushes into which Horatio had disappeared probably screened her fairly well from a distance. She swung her legs over the log, stood up, half-crouching, and edged along the bank until the bushes were between her and the path.

There was a small area of grass between the bushes and the edge of the bank, just wide enough for her to sit down, dangling her feet over the edge, just clear of the water. Horatio came out from under his bush and she seized his collar, bade him 'sit!' and 'be quiet!' and he flopped down beside her, looking expectantly into her face, as if he thought this was the beginning of an interesting game.

After what seemed remarkably little time, she heard the sound of heavy boots approaching along the path, and clamped one hand over Horatio's muzzle, holding tightly to his collar with the other, and waited for the steps to pass. The footsteps drew level, passed, then slowed, hesitated, returned, then stopped.

She held her breath, waiting, half afraid, half thinking herself a fool, for how was she to explain why she was hiding in the bushes without betraying to Mr Plomer that she feared he might mean her some harm! Worse still, what if he did mean to harm her?

'Miss Barnes?' the blacksmith enquired, sounding uncertain. 'Be yer all right? Is summat amiss?'

'No—no—nothing at all!' Caroline replied, trying to sound calm and collected. 'Horatio was interested in something here, and I came to see what it might be.'

'And what be it?'

Looking about for inspiration, Caroline's eyes fell upon the water below her feet. 'Fish!' she said firmly. 'He was looking at the fish in the stream.' There was, in fact, a small shoal quite near the bank.

'Yes, likely that'd be it,' Mr Plomer said. 'There's good fishing along here. It's Mester 'Artwell's water, and he don't mind folk taking a few, within reason. Not like some as I could mention!' he added darkly, and Caroline recollected the boy whom she had helped out of the other stream, across the meadows.

'Trouble is,' he continued, 'best fishes is in the preserved streams. Stands ter reason, I s'pose—streams what ain't fished is bound to have more in 'em. There's naught but tiddlers in Cornmill stream, but great whoppers in th' powder-mill water! There's some as thinks it worth th' risk o' getting caught to try for 'em—as yer knows yerself, o' course! It were good of yer to pull thet young lad out t'other day.'

'Oh!' Caroline exclaimed, disconcerted. 'I didn't think he'd tell anyone about that—he seemed very much afraid of being recognised.'

'There's some as yer can tell things to safely, and some as yer can't, and others what yer don't know, so yer says nought 'til yer does know,' Mr Plomer said sagely. 'Can yer get out o' there by yerself?'

'Yes, thank you,' Caroline replied politely, thinking that, although her fears at his approach now seemed remarkably silly, it might be as well to stay where she was for a while, protected by the bushes from a sudden attack, at least for long enough for her to jump into the stream and scream very loudly if necessary!

'I'll be getting back, then,' he said. 'Got plenty work ter do. Yer dropped yer liddle purse up the tower, didn' yer, and yer didn't pick up all yer money. 'Spose we startled yer. Any ways, yer left these—four shilling and two thripnies and two cartwheels. I'll put 'em on the log. Good day ter yer agen.' And, with that, he was off, back the way he had come, and Caroline was left to call her thanks after him and feel very stupid and embarrassed with herself for her unwarranted suspicions about his intentions.

'I am being extremely foolish,' she informed Horatio. 'What ever can be the matter with me? Surely I've never before suspected everyone about me of being involved in some villainy or other? After all, Mr Plomer may be a smuggler, but he's also a respected craftsman, and Captain of a bell-tower! Before I came here, I'd never have dreamed of thinking he might murder me, and I'm certain I thought no more evil of Mr Hartwell than that he was an arrogant man who treated his poor half-sister unjustly, and I've almost come to believe that I was wrong about that from the first. I really must stop imagining such dreadful, uncharitable things about people! Whatever would Mama say if she knew the terrible thoughts I've had this morning! She considers me sensible and intelligent, yet here I am, behaving like a character in a Gothic romance, seeing nothing but bad in the most respectable people, and assuming that even Mr Hartwell, who is, after all, a gentleman, might be . . . What do I think he might be? A spy? A traitor to his country? Just because I took a dislike to him when we first met. But I did take a dislike to him, and sometimes one's first impressions of a person turn out to be right . . .'

She stood up and edged her way back along the edge of the bank until a gap in the bushes allowed her to return to the path, where she paused to pick up her money from the log. Mr Plomer had left it in a neat pile, and she thought with some surprise that she must have been very agitated when he and Mr Hartwell discovered her in the tower, to leave such a large amount lying on the floor! Why, it was as much as a labouring man could earn in half a week, and the lack of the twopenny pieces must have made a considerable difference to the weight of her reticule, for these copper 'cartwheels' were of a most ridiculous size and heaviness.

She continued on her way, still worrying and wondering about Mr Hartwell and his mysterious activities until she reached Canons Grange, and only then recalled that she had gone out with a purpose which remained unfulfilled. She had completely forgotten about her embroidery silk, and would have to leave one flower unfinished until she could go into town again!

CHAPTER
TWELVE

IT APPEARED that the Harvest Supper had been held since time immemorial in a great barn which stood on the flat land at the foot of the hill on which Canons Grange was built. Caroline had noticed it with some curiosity during her comings and goings about the estate, but she had not explored it, for the doors always seemed to be barred and locked when she approached it. She suggested to Julia after luncheon that it would be interesting to visit it, and see what sort of a setting it would make for the entertainment, and Julia, considering herself much indebted to Caroline for advising her to follow a course of action which accorded in any case with her own wishes —that is, to marry Major Bridges if he offered—was in an amenable mood and actually showed some enthusiasm for the expedition, all the more because it involved only a short walk of a quarter-mile or so.

The barn was enormous. On the outside, it appeared to be merely a long rectangle of black clapboarding with a red-tiled roof. A jaunty weathervane of a ploughman with his plough and a yoke of oxen perched on one gable, and very large pairs of doors opened in the middle of each side, opposite to one another. Inside, it was more complex, for it was aisled, with two rows of great timber pillars, each the squared-off trunk of a whole tree, supporting a roof-structure of posts and beams. Mr Howard the steward was standing just within the open pair of doors as they entered, supervising the clearing of a year's accumulation of odds and ends, and he greeted them with a great deal of pleasure, being only too happy to point out the more important features of the building, and for a time there was much talk of king-posts and weatherbraces and twelfth- or thirteenth-century origin for the barn. 'Although it must have been re-roofed later, I think, or at least altered,' he added.

'But what is it used for?' Caroline asked, gazing about her. As far as she could see in the rather dim interior, there was virtually nothing in it at all now that the odds and ends had been carried off by the labourers.

'Well, when the Abbey still existed, it was used for storing the tithes of wheat and barley and so forth,' Mr Howard explained, 'There'd have been enough to provide bread and beer for all the canons and their servants and workers about the Abbey, and it went on being used in much the same way by the family who bought the Abbey from King Henry, until their manor house burned down and they went away. Well, to be honest, there's no real need for it any more. We use it as a cart-shed and a general store for bits and bobs which might be lost or spoiled if they were left in the open. Mr Hartwell sells the grain crops almost straight from the fields these days. There'll be turnips and such-like down one end later, but only what won't go into the barns nearer the house.'

Mr Howard seemed apologetic that he could not state that the barn still served a purpose so important that it was indispensable, and Caroline obviously pleased him very much when she said with genuine feeling, 'But what does it matter whether there's any use for it or not, when it's so fine and so very old? Why, it's like a primitive church, I do declare! You can imagine that our Saxon forebears must have built their churches just like this.'

'Indeed, yes!' Mr Howard responded, beaming. 'That's just what Mr Hartwell says. Someone wanted to buy it from him a while back, to pull it down for the timber and the tiles, but he wouldn't hear of it. He said he'd rather pull down the house and live in the barn, if he were ever forced to choose between them!'

'How ridiculous,' Julia commented. 'Robert does say the oddest things sometimes! As if one could live in a barn! I suppose he was joking. He does make jokes sometimes, but it's never very easy to tell if he's serious or not, for he says the most silly things as if he were in earnest.'

Caroline could not help but agree with her, albeit privately, but she felt sure that Mr Hartwell had not been joking about the barn, and once more her feelings towards him warmed and moved a little further from dislike and a few shades nearer to affection, although she was still not aware just how far that movement had advanced.

'I really don't see,' Julia continued, walking about the barn with exaggerated care to preserve her skirts from coming into contact with anything, 'how one could actually eat supper in here. It's so dusty and dirty, and the floor is just earth. How can they dance on it? There's no light, either—not a window in the place, and nowhere to hang chandeliers!'

'The women will be cleaning out this afternoon,' Mr Howard replied, looking a little annoyed at her criticism. 'Tomorrow they'll decorate with leaves and flowers, and we'll hang candle-lanterns about and sand the floor. It's been good enough for harvest supper as long as it's stood here, even if it's not a grand ballroom.'

'It could be made very attractive,' Caroline said soothingly, her imagination at work, 'if we hung wreaths and garlands of flowers and greenery from post to post, and across the beams. Would the women mind if we helped with the decorating, do you think?'

'They'd be only too pleased!' Mr Howard replied with a smile. 'In the old days, the ladies from the house always took charge of the preparations, but we've had to manage as best we could since Lady Hartwell went away. We were thinking we'd have to go on until she comes home, or Mr Hartwell marries, Miss Hartwell having lived away for all these years . . .'

It took a little enthusiastic talk by Caroline from time to time during the rest of the day to bring Julia round to the idea that it might be quite amusing to see whether the barn might be made to look something like a ballroom, but she eventually warmed to the notion, and the two young ladies spent most of Friday supervising and helping with the making of garlands from the quantities of greenery and flowers provided by the Canons Grange gardeners, or gathered from the hedgerows and cottage gardens by the children. There was also a number of corn-dollies of various shapes and designs, made by the older women, to hang among them when they had been wound round the pillars and looped along the beams.

By the late afternoon the barn had been transformed into a huge leafy bower, and a large number of lanterns had been brought in, fitted with candles, and hung from nails in the beams which had obviously been used for this purpose many times before.

Caroline was alone in the barn, the others having gone outside for tea and bread and butter, up a ladder, fixing a large wreath of corn, flowers and hawthorn berries to the centre of a beam, when Mr Hartwell walked in. He had been to London on some errand or other, and, having just returned, had come to see how things were progressing.

'"*Bring flowering garlands to me, that I may try a bout with love!*"' he said to her.

She eyed him warily through the rungs of the ladder, aware that he was quoting, yet failing to see anything apposite about the quotation. 'I'm hoping that Julia will find all this sufficiently interesting to wish to do it again in future,' she said matter-of-factly, conscious of an undeniable feeling of pleasure at the sight of his up-turned face.

'You look remarkably lovely up there, framed in greenery, rather like a dryad in some primaeval forest,' he said in a prosaic tone, which was in comic contrast to his sentiment. 'Your father sends his paternal greetings, and is glad to hear that you are well and happy.'

'Oh, have you seen him? How is he?' Caroline asked, feeling a pang of guilt that she had not written to her family, or even thought much about them. 'Are all at home well?' She wondered where Mr Hartwell had encountered her father, and then concluded, without really considering the matter, that he had probably taken her advice and gone to see Mr Barnes about a loan.

'Miss Alice Barnes has a sniffle, and Mr Thomas Barnes a sprained wrist, the ginger cat has had kittens —much to the surprise of those who thought her a tom—and your mother is resolved to move to Dulwich this week. Last week it was Brixton, and the week before, if I recollect correctly, Edgware. Your father is in excellent health. May I assist you to descend from your perch?'

Caroline replied that she thought she could manage, and backed carefully down the ladder, but Mr Hartwell moved round to stand behind her at the foot of it, complimenting her in earnest tones on the neatness of her ankles, which made her colour, the female ankle not being considered a suitable subject for comment in City circles, and she found herself descending virtually into his arms, for he had put a hand on either side of the ladder to steady it.

'I really do not require assistance, thank you,' she said over her shoulder.

'Better safe than sorry,' he replied with just a faint trace of amusement in his voice.

'Precisely,' Caroline said acidly, and stopped while still only half-way down the ladder, determined not to move until he did.

'Ah, a battle of wills!' he exclaimed joyfully. 'Now, what shall we do if tomorrow night arrives, with all our guests, and you and I are still firmly fixed in the middle of the floor? D'you think they'll pass us a little food and drink from time to time, and contrive to dance round us, or will they politely pretend we're not here? What explanation shall we offer them for this strange state of affairs?'

'You may tell them what you will,' Caroline replied coolly. 'I shall merely remark that some gentlemen can be remarkably stubborn in putting forward their attentions when they have been told quite clearly that they are unwelcome.'

'I see,' he said. 'Is that your final and irrevocable decision?'

'Oh, for Heaven's sake!' Caroline exclaimed angrily. 'Do have done with all this foolishness! The women will be coming back in a moment, and they'll think we've taken leave of our senses.'

'Ah! Not irrevocable! Good.' Mr Hartwell remarked quietly to himself. 'In that case, I shall, of course, act in accordance with your wishes, but pray, dearest Caroline, do not fall as you descend. I should be most upset if you broke your slender white neck, and Horatio would be quite devastated.'

With that, he looked critically at the footing of the ladder, apparently decided it would do, and walked away to the far end of the barn. Caroline descended and busied herself at the other end, untangling a garland which had been abandoned without proper care when its makers were called to tea.

Presently the workers came back in twos and threes from their refreshment, and the barn was soon full again of cheerful voices and bustling figures. Two men brought in a big sheaf of corn, and there was much earnest discussion with Mr Hartwell about whether the old hook was good enough to support it, or if a new one should be put in. Mr Hartwell made a pragmatic decision by seizing the hook and pulling himself clear of the ground, suspended from it, and pronounced it as good as ever. He then took off his coat, rolled up his shirt-sleeves, and helped to set up the barrels of ale which were trundled in from the cart which had delivered them.

Caroline continued to organise the floral decorations, assisted by Julia, who had actually volunteered to go and bespeak more flowers from the gardeners, and had returned carrying a basket containing at least two dozen blooms, and followed by a boy with another hundred or so.

'It really does begin to look quite pleasant,' Julia observed, placing a rose carefully into one side of a wreath. It fell out again almost directly, but one of the women hastily stuck it in again before the wreath was carried off to be hung, and Julia did not notice.

Eventually the decorations were finished, the floor swept and sanded, the trestles and benches set up, and everyone stood back to admire their handiwork.

'Ar,' said Mr Warrener, who, although he worked for Lord Cressing, not Mr Hartwell, had apparently attached himself to the proceedings, 'That looks a fair treat, and if'n the food's as fair to the stummick as the barn is to the eye, termorrer night'll be a feast will live in Istry. That's what!'

'Yes,' replied Mr Hartwell. 'Now, everyone—look about you. Have we forgotten anything?' Everyone obediently looked about. The corn sheaf was in place, the barrels of ale were set up, the serving-tables for the food were there, and the stools for the village band. The lanterns were hanging on their nails, and the benches and trestle tables stood in orderly rows.

There was complete silence for a moment, as nobody could think of anything forgotten, and then Julia's flower once again fell from its wreath, and landed with an audible plop at Mr Hartwell's feet. He picked it up almost absent-mindedly, then said, 'Well, if there's nothing missing, we may as well all go home. Thank you for your efforts, and for all the baking yet to come. The ingredients for the pies and so on are all ready and waiting in the kitchen up at the house, if you haven't already collected them, and I look forward to helping you eat the results, and to seeing you all and your families tomorrow night!'

As everyone began to go home, talking and laughing as they went, Julia hastened to enquire of Mr Howard if his gig were still outside, and, if so, if she might beg a ride up to the house. He called across to enquire if Caroline would like to be driven home, but she declined gracefully, saying she would prefer to walk. Too late, when Mr Howard and Julia had gone, she found that the servants from the house who had been helping had gone too, and she was left alone with Mr Hartwell, who walked across to her and held out the flower which had fallen from the wreath. It was a red rose.

'May I make my apologies, with this entirely suitable flower, for annoying you?' he asked, apparently quite seriously. 'I'm not much of a hand at flirtation and so forth. My intentions are of the best, but nothing seems to come out quite as I intended.'

Caroline was quite taken aback by this speech, and for the first time it occurred to her that an appearance of arrogance is often a cover for feelings of embarrassment or inadequacy, and she was even more convinced that she had possibly misjudged him from the start.

Unfortunately, he suddenly resumed his usual manner, presented the rose to her with a graceful bow, and enquired sardonically, 'Shall you now fall into my arms with protestations of eternal friendship, or shall we merely walk home together in a sober and reflective consideration of the beauties of the evening, punctuated by earnest conversation on topics of grave philosophical weight, such as the likelihood of blackberry pie for dinner?'

'With cream or with custard?' Caroline replied coolly, decided that in all probability Mr Hartwell's arrogance was only a cover for more arrogance, but she accepted the rose, and, when his hand rested against hers as it was transferred, her heart beat a little faster and she avoided catching his eye.

But the conversation on the way home was entirely concerned with furry animals, for Mr Warrener had not come to the barn merely to admire, but to speak with its owner, and he materialised beside Mr Hartwell as he and Caroline left the barn, and walked along with them in the twilight, explaining a plan he had for extending his warrening activities into one of Mr Hartwell's fields which marched with Lord Cressing's, with the aid of Mr Hartwell's underkeeper, who wished to learn the profession, and then he continued all the way to the house talking about ferrets.

Mr Hartwell was deeply interested in the man's talk, and gave him almost his full attention, but he also caught Caroline's hand and drew her arm through his, pressing it against him, still holding her hand in a firm clasp, so that when, from time to time, afflicted with a sense of the impropriety of walking thus arm-in-arm with him, she attempted to withdraw, he would not let her do so. This, in the curious civil war between prudence and inclination going on within her, both troubled and pleased her.

The following evening at the harvest supper, there was a positive battery of blackberry pies. In fact, the quantity of food set out on the tables in the barn quite amazed Caroline when she arrived there with Julia promptly at six o'clock, as Mr Hartwell had requested. They made quite an entrance, for the labourers and their wives and children were already assembled and sitting on the benches on either side of the long tables, which were now covered with white cloths, barely visible between dishes and platters of every size and description, all piled with food.

All the people were dressed in their best, the children well scrubbed, the men with their hair combed and slicked down with water, and the women wearing their ribbons and fairings, and most with their hair persuaded by a night and a day in curl-papers or rags to fall into ringlets.

Julia had not particularly wished to dress formally for the evening, but Caroline had said that she intended to do so, for it was a great occasion for the estate workers and they would be hurt if the gentry did not bother to put on their finery.

'As if such folk could be hurt! Why, they don't have fine feelings as we do,' Julia replied scornfully, to which Caroline replied a little sharply, 'They most certainly do, but they can rarely afford to show them!'

Julia said nothing to that, but she came down from her room when it was time to go to the barn dressed in white gauze over blue peau-de-soie, with her hair ornamented with pale blue ribbons and feathers, a moonstone necklace, and a matching bracelet over one of her long white gloves.

Caroline was wearing a deep rose satin with a fine silk overgown in a paler shade of the same colour, and carried one of her cashmere shawls, for she thought the barn would probably be draughty. Martha had pinned two pink roses on the crown of her head, and her ringlets fell from beneath them in a most becoming manner.

Mr Hartwell was also formally dressed in a dark blue
tail-coat and white knee-breeches, with crisp white frills
at his wrists and on his shirt-front, silk stockings and
dancing-slippers, which surprised Caroline, who had
never seen him wear other than pantaloons and boots on
his nether limbs.

They were joined at the barn by the Rector, but not
his wife, who seldom felt well enough to dine out with
the gentry, and never attended functions such as this
evening's festivity. Nobody was particularly surprised to
find that Major Bridges and Captain Marsh had come
with the Rector. Julia was, of course, delighted, but
Caroline was not, and did her best to evade Captain
Marsh as much as possible.

At Mr Hartwell's invitation, the Rector said Grace,
and then the feasting began. It was amazing how rapidly
the food disappeared, although Caroline had thought
there was an inordinate amount of it, and then the dishes
were cleared away, the tables disassembled and stacked
outside, the benches ranged along the walls, and the
band, after wiping its mouth on the backs of its hands,
produced its instruments, took up its position, mugs of
ale handily placed under its stools, and the dancing
began.

It was not, of course, the sort of dancing which
Caroline had learned in her childhood and indulged in at
parties and balls, but the old-fashioned country dancing
in circles or long lines, with much clapping more or less
in time to the music, and showy capering from the
younger men, who whirled their partners clean off their
feet at every opportunity.

Some proper chairs had been provided for the gentry
at the end of the barn furthest from the band, which
Caroline considered a thoughtful arrangement, as the
scraping of two fiddles and the stridency of three or four
brass instruments would have been uncomfortable at

close quarters. She found the rhythm infectious, and her feet seemed to tap of their own volition whenever she forgot to keep them still.

Mr Hartwell had been prancing, swinging, advancing and retiring with the best of them from the start with a succession of stout matrons, and Major Bridges, after a few false starts and hesitations, also plunged into a lively Sellenger's Round, but Captain Marsh and the Rector contented themselves with nodding and foot-tapping while they kept the ladies company, the Captain trying repeatedly to engage Caroline in conversation, which, because of the noise, necessitated almost shouting, and gave her a good excuse to fail to hear him most of the time.

'Come, Caroline!' Mr Hartwell said peremptorily, appearing before her in his shirt-sleeves, his hair far less smooth than usual from his exertions. 'Will you not honour the company by dancing?'

'But I don't know the figures . . .' Caroline protested unconvincingly, allowing him to take her hands and draw her to her feet. 'You'll have to tell me what to do.'

They took their places in the middle of a long set, while Major Bridges and Julia, fired by their example, joined another. It was, in fact, quite easy to follow the dance, for the women on either side of Caroline guided her forward or back and turned her in the right direction whenever necessary, and by the time she and Mr Hartwell reached the top-couple position, she had learned by observation what to do, and went galloping sideways down the middle, back and down again in Mr Hartwell's arms like an old hand.

After that, of course, she had no respite while the dancing lasted, and was partnered in turn by one of the stable-lads (red-faced but triumphant at his own daring), a tenant-farmer, Captain Marsh (who danced very badly, forever turning the wrong way and having to be pushed about by his neighbours), a gamekeeper, a labourer, and the coachman, with Mr Hartwell taking more than his fair share of turns in between. It was all great fun, but tiring, and eventually all but the most active retired to the benches, red-faced and gasping, and there was a general call for a song, to which a burly ploughman eventually responded after some 'Come on, then, Eli!' and pushing from his neighbours, with a rich bass rendering of 'Heart of Oak', which was loudly cheered. This was followed by several more efforts by a variety of performers, the two females among them warbling sentimental airs, but the men choosing hearty sporting or patriotic songs with choruses, in which everyone joined.

There came a time when nearly all the children were asleep on their mothers' laps or on the floor against or under the benches, and then a voice called for 'Mester 'Artwell', to be echoed by a growing chorus from the rest, and Mr Hartwell took up his stance with one foot on a small cask, looking, Caroline thought secretly, very handsome and romantic in his white shirt, which had long ago shed its stiff collar and cravat, and sang 'Britons, Strike Home' in a true and powerful tenor.

When the cheers and applause had died down afterwards, he thanked everyone for the work they had done to make the evening possible, and particularly for coming, and then led the company in 'Rule, Britannia'. After that, the Rector pronounced a blessing, and Mr Hartwell bade everyone a good night, and invited anyone who still felt hungry to take home some of the left-overs. There was quite a lot, as Caroline was surprised to see, until it dawned on her that the food which had mysteriously appeared on the serving-tables was not left-overs, but reinforcements.

It was, for labouring country folk, very late by then, and the assembly soon dispersed, the food vanishing with them. Mr Hartwell stood by the door to shake their hands and most took the opportunity to thank him. Before long, the gentry were left alone, except for Mr Howard, who was extinguishing those candles which had not already burned out.

'Did you enjoy yourself?' Caroline asked Julia with mischievous intent, for the girl had kept up her attitude of ennui at the whole business until quite far into the evening.

'It was not as unpleasant as I expected,' Julia admitted, demurely smoothing her gown and avoiding her cousin's eye, but then she was distracted by a sight which made her stare wide-eyed, her mouth dropping open in a round O. Major Bridges had marched over to Mr Hartwell, who was shrugging himself into his coat, and was engaged in a serious, low-voiced speech to him.

'What about?' Mr Hartwell asked loudly. Major Bridges made a further low-voiced speech.

'By all means,' Mr Hartwell replied, again in a loud and cheerful tone. 'Any time you like. You have my blessing!'

'But don't you want to—er . . .' Major Bridges asked in an agitated voice.

'Time for all that later,' Mr Hartwell replied. 'First things first. Proposal first, settlements after. Ah, you're off now, Rector? Good night to you, and thank you for coming.' The Rector was indeed departing, and, as they had come in his carriage, the two officers had perforce to go with him, Captain Marsh gazing sadly upon Caroline, as if to signify that he had at last realised that she had no encouragement to offer him, and Major Bridges looking quite bemused.

'Oh, Caro!' Julia gasped, seizing her cousin's arm with both hands and well-nigh throttling it. 'He didn't say No! He said dearest James had his blessing! Oh, dearest Robert!' She released Caroline in order to run to her brother, flinging her arms about him and standing on tiptoe to kiss his cheek.

'Dearest, dearest Robert! Oh, thank you!' she cried.

'Yes, all right then,' he replied, his eyebrows rising quizzically. 'There's no need to attack me!' fending off an attempt at a second embrace. 'You'd best be off to bed, or you'll be late for church in the morning.' With this dampening speech, he disengaged himself and went off with Mr Howard, talking about turnips, and leaving the ladies to go home without him in the carriage, which had been waiting outside for the past ten minutes.

CHAPTER
THIRTEEN

CAROLINE AWOKE with a start and lay tensed, listening, conscious that some unusual sound had disturbed her, yet not sure what it could be. Her eyes turned towards the partly-open window, which was visible only as a lighter patch in the darkness of her room, spangled lightly with a few stars.

There was a single scrunching sound, followed by a faint murmur of, 'Keep him on the grass, damn yer! Have yer no more sense than ter let him step on gravel?' Caroline could make out the words only because she was already straining to hear any sound there might be, but she felt that she knew the voice. It was deep and gruff, and the slurred vowels put her in mind of Will Plomer —or Mr Warrener, for that matter, although his voice, as far as she could recollect, was a trifle less deep.

The silence which followed was, somehow, not silence at all, although she could hear no particular sound. There was just a consciousness of living creatures of some kind—human or animal—breathing, waiting and listening beneath her window. After a few minutes, the tension became too much for her, and she slipped out of bed and crept over to the window, keeping to one side and peering down obliquely to see if anything could be seen.

Down the valley, James and John sounded the four quarters, followed by Gabriel, sounding three sonorous strokes, and there was a slight stirring below, just enough for her to be able to locate dark figures standing on the grass beyond the terrace.

Suddenly a small part of the scene became appreciably

lighter, but she realised that it was because someone had
lit candles in the library only when there was a stealthy
sound of a window opening, and a quite voice breathed,
'Will? I told you to go to the back!' It was Mr Hartwell.

'Cobbles is too noisy,' replied the original voice.
'Here's yer passel. Red, yer said, and red he is!'

A single figure moved swiftly forward from the group
of shadows, and the candlelight briefly illuminated a
pale face and hair which glinted as their owner stepped
lightly over the gravel and out of sight, presumably into
the library through the long window.

'Well done, Will!' Mr Hartwell whispered. 'Leave
the rest in the usual place. Thank you, and good
night!'

There was again the stealthy sound of the window-
latch, closing this time, and the dark shadows on the
grass melted away, but Caroline remained at the window, listening, and presently she heard the sound of
light hooves on the gravel, far down the drive.

'Well, no great mystery about them!' she thought.
'They were the smugglers, nighthawking, but who was it
that went into the library?'

She sat down on the broad window-sill and considered
what she should do next, recalling the warning Mr
Hartwell had given her against prying into the affairs of
the smugglers, but it appeared that they had only been
delivering a 'parcel' to him—a man, that is! Who on
earth could it be this time? Another banker, perhaps?'

Perplexed, she bit her thumb, torn between a desire to
solve the mystery, and a conscience which told her that it
was none of her business, and she ought to go back to
bed and not concern herself in her host's private concerns. On the other hand, she had so many doubts about
Mr Hartwell's secret activities that she felt an urgent
need to resolve them, if at all possible. It now seemed
ludicrous that she had been so firmly convinced that he

was arrogant and odious, and all the more painful that, having at last realised how she had misjudged him, she should now be tormented by the fear that he might be a villain in a far more serious way.

At present, she felt that her mind was equally balanced between believing what he had told her, and disbelieving it, particularly about Mr Rothschild's visit, and this, being another of a similar sort, might give her an indication of the truth or otherwise of his explanation about the former midnight meeting. If only she could hear something of what passed down in the library, she might be able to judge whether that earlier visit had really been about transferring government money to Portugal, or, as she had suspected at the time, about a private loan, or possibly about something else entirely. If, by any chance, Mr Hartwell was up to no good in some way, then surely she had a duty to do something about it which outweighed her duty to her host?

'After all,' she thought, 'I know that there was a spy here before, and Lord Cressing seemed concerned, when he told me about him, that Bonaparte, might have sent another to replace him. Surely, if the camp and the powder-mill were important enough to warrant the presence of a spy, the French would not leave them without one after losing the original! What if this man who has just come is . . . Oh, dear!'

Her eyes filled with tears, and she pressed her hands against them, trying to stop the flow. 'Oh, Robert, Robert!' she thought. 'If you're a traitor, I shall have to tell Lord Cressing! I can't bear it! I don't want to know! I don't believe you are, but I must know!' And she sobbed fitfully, clenching and unclenching her hands, then made up her mind.

'I have to know,' she said quietly. 'One way or the other, I have to know the truth about him. I can't go on like this, wondering, doubting, worrying . . . And if he is a traitor, and he kills me for spying on him, it might even be the best thing . . . !'

Having made her decision, she moved swiftly, groping for her wrapper and pulling it on, then throwing a shawl about her shoulders, crossing the ends in front of her and tying them at the back of her waist, so there would be no trailing part to trip her, for this time she meant to find her way down the stairs in the wall without a candlestick to drop.

It was very dark in the corridor, and it seemed an age before her fingers, sliding silently about on the panelling, found the small knob and twisted it. For a moment she thought the door was locked, but suddenly the latch clicked, sounding unnaturally loud in the dark and silent house, and she waited, hardly daring to breathe, for some response from the room below.

Silence. She slipped through the opening and closed the door behind her as gently as she could remembering that last time she had left it open, and there had been a draught up the stairs, which might possibly be felt in the library. She paused for a few seconds, listening, and waiting for her eyes to become accustomed to pitch darkness, and presently made out a tiny blur of grey below, where the little window opened on the garden. Cautiously, with a hand on the wall on either side of her, she tiptoed down, feeling for each step and making sure that there was nothing on the tread before she put any weight down on it.

How slowly she moved! She began to fear that she would reach the bottom too late to hear anything, but she dared not try to go more quickly. At last she reached the little window, paused, and glanced out, but there was only the lighter greyness of the night, with a few leaves of the ivy which covered the wall silhouetted against it. How many steps to the bottom? She could not remember, and so had to creep on down, feeling now for the edge of each step as well as the tread, and gradually she became conscious of a faint, uneven murmuring. Voices!

Then, at last, her foot found a wider, flat surface, which stretched clear across to a wall which stubbed her toes, and she knew she was at the bottom. The voices were louder now, but she could not hear what they were saying, so she felt for the door-knob, meaning to hold on to it to prevent the door from opening and betraying her. Where . . . ? Ah, there it was!

Cautiously, she took a firm hold of it, then pressed her ear to the wooden panel. The voices became clearer, and, as she listened, she found she could distinguish, not two, as she had expected, but three speakers!

One of them was Mr Hartwell. His cool, ironic voice was unmistakable, and the second seemed familiar, but did not say enough for her to place it, or to distinguish any more of it than that it was pleasant, and a shade deeper in tone than Mr Hartwell's.

The third voice was not unlike Mr Hartwell's, but its owner spoke more quickly, yet paused from time to time, apparently in mid-sentence, as if seeking the right word, or considering carefully what he had to say, and there was something odd about the cadences of it. Caroline tried to puzzle out what it was that sounded not quite right, and eventually decided that the rhythm of the man's speech was somehow different, as though he placed emphasis on the wrong syllables. Once she had realised that, she soon found that he never emphasised the first syllable of a word, and she also noticed that his speech seemed to go in little rushes, followed by a minute hesitation.

'He sounds like a foreigner,' she thought, her heart sinking. If only she could hear more clearly what was being said! Very cautiously, she turned the knob which was tightly clutched in her right hand, and eased the door open a crack. It made no sound, and there was no detectable draught, for which she thanked her foresight in shutting the door at the top of the stairs.

'*Je vous assure,*' she heard the third man say, '*que mon maître est devenu exaspéré avec notre ami . . .*' He spoke clearly and distinctly, as though to ensure that his auditors could understand him.

'French!' Caroline thought, losing the rest of the speech in the tumult of horror and emotion which flooded over her. 'Oh, merciful heavens! Whatever am I to do?'

Trembling, she forced herself to stand still and listen, but the stranger was no longer speaking. Mr Hartwell was now saying something in such rapid French that she could not follow it, her own command of the language being no better than that of any young English lady who had learned a little of it in the schoolroom, but had had no occasion to use it since.

The second man cut in, interrupting Mr Hartwell in mid-speech, saying in English, 'I'm sure our guest will talk more easily when he has eaten.'

Caroline, in her agitation, missed the opportunity to recognise his voice, so tantalisingly familiar, and resumed listening carefully only in time to hear Mr Hartwell say, 'But of course. Let us retire to the dining-room.'

There was a sound of movement, of chairs being pushed back, of steps across the floor, and then the library door opened and closed. Someone had taken the branch of candles, for the room was suddenly dark, and Caroline was left in a state of unbearable tension, hardly knowing what to do. She shut the door in the panelling and sat down on the bottom step to consider.

At first, she was half-determined to follow the men and listen at the dining-room door, but the chances of discovery, common sense told her, would be much increased if she did. Possibly a servant would come to wait at table, and find her, or one of the men might open the door for some reason, and she could recall no possible hiding-place in the passage outside the dining-room.

Then she remembered that the library and dining-room had been formed by dividing the old Great Hall of the medieval house, and she wondered if the division had been made with panelling. It took only a moment to open the 'secret' door again and enter the library, and then she stopped, recollecting that she did not know how the little door opened from outside the room. What if someone came, and she could not reopen it again in time to hide? By feeling the outside, she discovered that the door was concealed by shelves filled with books—real ones, not fakes, and it was easy enough to put one of them on the floor between the door and its jamb, preventing it from closing.

With her means of retreat secured, she tiptoed across the room to the far wall, and felt along it, seeking an area of panelling where there were no shelves of books, and eventually found a place under the portrait of her aunt, Julia's mother, and pressed her ear against it. She could hear nothing. Obviously, either a solid partition wall had been put in, or the heavy panelling in the dining-room was as thick as it looked. She retreated in good order to the foot of the little staircase again, and reconsidered. She could not listen outside the dining-room door, or through the wall, so what else was there?

Of course! The dining-room had a window! She hesitated, biting her lip, trying to think of any possible danger of discovery if she tried listening outside that window, but none occurred to her. The smugglers were gone, and no one else was likely to be about outside. There was no reason why any servant should go out on to the terrace—if, indeed, any of the servants were out of bed at this time of night! If anyone did approach, the gravel on the terrace would give warning of his coming . . .

Once more she entered the library, and carefully put her book-doorstop in place and pulled the door against it to wedge it. By now, her eyes were sufficiently accustomed to the dark to be able to discern not only the lighter patches of the windows, but the darker shapes in the dark room which were the furniture, and to reach the window behind the table without knocking against anything. She eased up the window-catch slowly and very cautiously, and found that it was slightly greasy. Obviously someone else before her had found good reason for wishing to open it quietly!

The window opened easily, and she stepped outside and shivered as the night air struck with chilly fingers through her wrapper and shawl. The gravel hurt her bare feet, but she persevered and moved like a shadow along the house wall to the neighbouring window of the dining-room, and went as close to it as she could. It was closed and dark, but a crack of light showed at one edge, where the drawn curtains had left a gap, but that gap was so narrow that she could see nothing through it.

At first she did not seem to be able to get close enough to the window to put her ear to it, for, unlike the library windows, those of the dining-room were not made to open, and a shrub of some kind was growing directly under this one. She tried leaning against it, but it was springy and pushed her back, and parting its branches to try to push her way between them only resulted in a scratched arm. Nor could she get behind it, for it seemed to cling to the wall, as if determined to protect its owner from prying ears and eyes. Thwarted, she moved along to the next window, regretting that she had not worn her bedroom slippers, at least, for the gravel was very sharp and uncomfortable to walk on.

This time, she had better luck. There was no shrub below this window, only a fancy tile edging of some kind, which stubbed her toes most viciously but allowed her to get close enough to the window to press her ear against it. She could hear voices, but not well enough to distinguish what they were saying, and she was surprised, for she had not thought that glass would prevent sound passing through quite as well as this. Then she recollected that the curtains, which were drawn right across this window, were very thick, and were probably muffling the voices as well.

It was very frustrating, and she could not decide what to do next. There seemed to be no point in standing there in the cold, with the gravel cutting her feet, so she limped back to the library and sat down in the darkness to think.

What exactly had Lord Cressing said that day on the top of the tower? She could recall pretty well the part about the spy, and looking out for any person who seemed curious about the camp and the powder-mill, but what had he said when she mentioned Mr Hartwell's comings and goings? 'Your cousin Robert is not a spy.' Yes, he had certainly said that, but there had been something else about 'He very well could be if . . .' something-or-other. No, however hard she tried, she could not recollect the exact words, which was irritating.

She was, however, quite sure that Lord Cressing had not given any reason for his belief that Mr Hartwell was not a spy, and she assumed that it had probably not occurred to him that a gentleman of his acquaintance, a landowner and the son of a Baron, could possibly be a criminal. She had noticed that most men seemed to be quite amazed to discover that one of their own circle was not all that he had appeared to be! No—Lord Cressing was an admirable man, and might safely be left to decide the fate of a spy once he was apprehended, but he was not infallible, and Caroline felt that she would need to know his reasons for exonerating Mr Hartwell before she could accept the verdict.

'That's the answer, of course!' she thought. 'I must go to Lord Cressing and tell him all about it! In fact, I must go now, so that he may come here and catch the Frenchman! In that case, I must hurry, for the man may not be staying here very long.'

Obviously, she could not set off for Pinnacles barefoot and dressed only in her night-clothes, so she made her way back to the door behind the bookshelves, put her temporary door-stop back in its proper place, and carefully closed the door behind her before starting to go back up the stairs.

'Now—just a moment! How am I to get to Pinnacles?' she thought, and sat down on the stairs to consider the matter. She knew two ways to Lord Cressing's house —one of them along the ridge and across the fields to the foot of his garden, and the other, which she had not travelled, but could deduce, by road—the road to the end of the town, and then along the turnpike which led up into the Forest. The latter would be the easier way in the dark, but much longer, for it would be two sides of a triangle.

Thinking the matter over, she rather doubted her ability to find her way to Pinnacles across country in the dark, and felt very apprehensive about going alone in the middle of the night, for she was, after all, a city-bred female, and the country was still an unknown and rather frightening place, particularly at night.

'Perhaps I'd better go to someone else for help!' she thought. 'Colonel Long—oh, but I don't know where he lives, unless it's at the camp, and I'm certainly not going there by myself! I think I'd best go to the Rectory. After all, the Rector will know what to do, and Lord Cressing is his son-in-law!'

That decided, she stood up and went on up the stairs. It took her a few seconds to locate the door-knob on the inside of the closed door, and it seemed to make a dreadful clatter in the silent house as she turned it, stepped out into the corridor, and closed the door behind her.

Even as she did so, she realised that something had gone wrong with her plan. She had left the corridor in darkness, but now it was dimly lit, and the light came from her bedroom. Someone had lighted the candles on her dressing-table, and left the door wide open!

Her first instinct was to run away, but she checked before she had done any more than jerk her body in response to the idea. Where could she run to? The house was locked up, and the only certain way she knew of to get out of it was through the library window. She stood staring at the open bedroom door, trying to decide where to go.

'I was beginning to wonder what had become of you!' a quiet, calm voice said from behind her. She spun round, and there was Mr Hartwell, standing in the corridor watching her. 'Did you manage to hear very much?' he enquired mildly.

Caroline was silent, surprised to find that she was not in the least afraid of him, but was simply nonplussed.

'The trouble is,' she said, 'I just don't know what to believe!'

'About what?' he enquired gravely.

'You.'

'Me?' He sounded surprised. 'In what respect?'

'You said—at least, you implied—that you're concerned in arranging for supplies for Sir Arthur Wellesley's army, and I can accept that it could be true, but then, on the other hand, it could be untrue . . . I've no way of telling!'

'You could take my word for it!'

'Yes. I should like to . . . It's just that it seems a little unlikely. Why should a man like you concern himself with things like that? I mean—a country gentleman . . . I thought such a person was interested only in his land and crops, his dogs and horses and guns. Why should you put yourself to the trouble of going about the country, worrying about oats and—and bootlaces?'

'Patriotism, possibly?' he offered consideringly. 'Perhaps the Horse Guards pay me well? They don't, actually. If I'm not doing that, what do you imagine I am doing?

'I don't know,' Caroline said wretchedly. 'Then there's Mr Rothschild . . .'

'Nathan Meyer? Yes? What about him?'

'Well—he could have come here for the reason you said, or for the reason I assumed—to lend you money, I mean—but it could have been for another reason . . .'

'You already have two perfectly good reasons, why put yourself to the trouble of seeking a third?'

'You warned me that I might put myself into danger by prying into your affairs . . .'

'I did nothing of the sort! I warned you against taking too much interest in the smugglers! I said nothing about my own concerns.'

'But I thought . . . Oh.' Caroline suddenly realised that this was quite true.

'It seems to me,' he observed judicially, 'that you've been letting your imagination run away with you. I'll admit that, at first glance, my behaviour is a little suspicious—sudden comings and goings, odd visitors at strange hours, no social chit-chat about where I've been or what I've been doing, but I've explained all that to you. Why do you still think I'm up to some sort of villainy?'

'Why did you meet Will Plomer in secret in the

bell-tower?' she flung at him, nettled by his light dismissal of the doubts which had tormented her.

'Does no obvious explanation occur to you? Surely you can think of a reason why I might have private business with a smuggler? Were you listening at the door that morning, by the way? If you were, you should know what we were discussing.'

'No, I was not listening!' she replied indignantly.

'I'll take your word for that, even if you're not prepared to accept mine,' he said evenly. 'But you were listening tonight? I thought you probably were. I told Will to come to the stable-yard tonight, so that there'd be no danger of disturbing you, but he prefers to do things his own way—an independent fellow, unfortunately!'

The conversation up to this point should have made Caroline feel very foolish to have harboured such ridiculous doubts and suspicions about a man with whom she was almost prepared to admit that she was in love, but, with feminine perversity, her reaction was, instead, one of irritation which now flared into sudden anger.

'You dismiss all my doubts and fears so easily, don't you, and sneer at me for suspecting you, but, pray, how do you explain away the Frenchman you are entertaining in your dining-room?

'He's not a Frenchman,' Mr Hartwell replied flatly.

'He is! I heard him speaking in French!'

'You probably also heard me speaking French—does that make me a Frenchman as well?'

'No, but you could be working for them!'

'For the French? Now, why on earth should I do that?'

Caroline suddenly thought of a very good reason, and one which would make such perfidy almost forgivable.

'Your parents are prisoners in France,' she said slowly, working it out aloud. 'That would give the French a

hold over you, would it not? They could threaten to
ill-treat, or even kill, your father, or your stepmother, or
your sister, unless you acted as a spy for them. You're in
exactly the right place—in the town where the army
camp and the powder-mill are sufficiently interesting to
them for them to keep a spy here before, but last year
they lost that spy! Now they have you, living here, above
suspicion, because you're a gentleman, and your family
has been here for generations . . .'

'Or maybe they've offered to free my father if I supply
them with a set of maps of Portugal, neatly marked with
the route which Sir Arthur intends to follow into Spain,'
Mr Hartwell continued for her. 'My dearest Caroline!
Your imagination is superb! You really should take up
novel-writing! Thank God you don't work for the
French yourself. That really is a remarkably good little
plot!'

'You're not working for Bonaparte, then,' Caroline
stated rather than asked.

'Certainly not!'

'Then why is there a Frenchman in your dining-
room?'

'You remind me of Horatio in pursuit of a beef
sandwich!' he observed. 'I repeat—he's not a Frenchman. Get dressed, and come down and meet him, if you
wish. You'll like him very much—he's a real charmer!'

'Really?' Caroline asked incredulously.

'By all means! I accept that I can't keep your delightful
little nose out of my business, so I can only make the best
of it and invite you in. With your imagination and
ingenuity, you'll probably be an asset! Come now—run
and put on something more suitable, and I'll take you
down. I promise not to push you off the church tower on
the way!'

Somehow, the final jocular remark convinced Caroline that he really did mean to take her into the heart of

the mystery and give her a true explanation. She could not account for her conviction, for it was as quixotic and unreasonable as her earlier fears and doubts, but it was with a much lighter heart that she hurried into her room and dressed herself, while Mr Hartwell waited patiently outside the closed door.

Fortunately, Martha believed in leaving everything ready for the morning before she went off duty for the night, and stays, shift, stockings and garters were all neatly laid out, ready to be put on, and a freshly-pressed frock hung ready in the closet. Caroline put them on, adding the inevitable shawl, with fingers made clumsy by haste and excitement. She did not pause to arrange her hair, but brushed it out and tied it back in a schoolgirlish fashion with a piece of ribbon, unaware that the escaping curls about her face were particularly becoming to her, but only concerned with being as quick as possible to make herself ready to face the solution to the mystery.

'Good heavens!' Mr Hartwell exclaimed when she emerged, dressed and ready, in a bare ten minutes. 'I thought every female required at least half an hour! Or is that only when a maid is in attendance?'

'Probably,' Caroline replied good-humouredly, suddenly concluding that most of his derogatory remarks about females were meant jokingly. It was difficult to tell, she decided, when a man was joking if he did so with a straight face.

She accompanied him downstairs by the more orthodox route along the gallery and down the main staircase, as quickly as he could possibly have desired, and approached the dining-room door with a pleasurable anticipatory feeling that all her doubts and fears were about to be resolved, and, in short, that All was About to be Revealed.

The two men were sitting at the table, talking quietly and amicably together in French over a glass of wine.

They rose as Caroline entered, a step or two ahead of Mr Hartwell, and regarded her with interest. One of them was Lord Cressing.

'Oh!' exclaimed Caroline, stopping so suddenly that Mr Hartwell almost cannoned into her. 'No wonder I thought your voice seemed familiar!'

Lord Cressing smiled, and added, 'And no wonder I was so sure that your cousin Robert couldn't be a spy! Good evening, Miss Barnes—or, rather, good morning!'

'Indeed, good morning!' she replied, conscious that this was a ridiculous hour for a social gathering, and turned her attention to the other man.

He was quite young, she thought, not more than a few years older than herself, and his hair was the brightest red that she had ever seen on anyone's head—not auburn or ginger, but a true fiery red, and his eyes were green. He was slightly built, with a natural grace in his movements which made the other two men appear clumsy, and, despite the fact that he must have crossed the North Sea recently in a small sailing-boat, and had probably been brought from the coast in three or four night-time journeys on the back of a pony, or even on foot, he was neatly dressed in a well-cut dark green coat and trousers, and his linen looked immaculate. He regarded Caroline with a most encouraging and heart-warmingly open admiration, and waited patiently to be presented.

'This gentleman,' Lord Cressing began, 'is travelling at present under the name of Smith. I'll admit it's an uncommonly unconvincing alias, but it was chosen by a man at the Foreign Office who is singularly lacking in imagination. I'm afraid it's the only name we are allowed to use for him at present, even if we knew his real identity, which we don't. I can only add to that the information that he's Russian.'

'Russian!' Caroline exclaimed. 'But we're at war with Russia.'

'Unfortunately,' said 'Mr Smith' in excellent—in fact, almost perfect—English. 'Otherwise I should be coming to London in comfort, quite openly, with a passport, instead of being hidden in barns by persons of doubtful honesty, along with a hodge-podge of miscellaneous parcels and casks. The word hodge-podge is correct in this context, is it not?' he added, looking with some amusement at Lord Cressing and Mr Hartwell, who were staring at him in open-mouthed astonishment.

'You speak English!' the latter said accusingly.

'Naturally. My country's government is not re-nowned for efficiency, but even they would hardly send a secret emissary to England who could not speak English!' He looked from one startled face to the other with a most infectious smile.

'Then why have we been speaking French all night?' asked Lord Cressing, puzzled.

'I thought you preferred it, as it's the language of diplomacy. It makes no difference to me—I speak as I am spoken to!'

'Mr Smith' transferred his attention back to Caroline, and said confidentially, 'I'm enchanted to make your acquaintance, Miss Barnes! These gentlemen have been discussing you with great animation, and I gather that they are filled with admiration for your courage and tenacity! Lord Cressing thinks you should be told *all* about Mr Hartwell's secret activities, so that you may be a help to him instead of a hindrance. It appears that his lordship tells his wife *everything*, which may or may not be a wise thing to do. I am not acquainted with the lady, so cannot give an opinion.'

'Yes,' Caroline replied non-committally, deciding to consider what he had told her later. 'But if you're a Russian, what are you doing in Mr Hartwell's dining-room in the middle of the night?'

'Shall we be seated?' 'Mr Smith' indicated the chairs about the dining-table. They all sat down, and Mr Hartwell poured a glass of wine apiece.

'You know the situation regarding Russia,' Lord Cressing began, recovering his customary unobtrusive domination of the gathering. 'The Emperor Alexander signed a treaty with Bonaparte at Tilsit last year. This was not approved by the great majority of his subjects, but Alexander does as he pleases . . .'

'The result has been most unfortunate for Russia,' 'Mr Smith' took over smoothly. 'Our foreign trade is ruined. We've acquired Finland, but most of us didn't particularly want it in the first place. There is grave discontent throughout the Empire, and Alexander Pavlovich's mother is barely on speaking terms with him! Now, however, the Emperor is beginning to be disenchanted with Bonaparte. The upstart Corsican proposes to marry one of the Emperor's sisters—he is not, it appears, particular about which one—and the whole Imperial family resents his presumption to the uttermost. The Emperor begins to think that he may have made a mistake, yet does not wish to break with Bonaparte, because that means fighting him again, and Russia has not done very well in that respect in the past!'

Caroline drank all this in, wide-eyed, and volunteered, 'So he needs to find a way to wriggle out of his treaty obligations without upsetting Bonaparte too much.'

'Mr Smith' smiled encouragingly upon her, as upon a favourite pupil, and said, 'He's not quite that far advanced yet. No—the main trouble in Russia at present is financial. The best of our trade was with England, and Alexander would like that to restart—unofficially, of course, and without his knowledge, naturally! That's why I'm here.'

Caroline thought about it, biting her lip. 'That would make a sizeable hole in Bonaparte's Continental System,' she said pensively. 'If the Baltic is reopened for trade, it would be a great help to the Navy—ships' masts and hemp are becoming very scarce and expensive!'

'Miss Barnes's father is a City merchant,' Mr Hartwell put in parenthetically.

'But Bonaparte would soon see what was happening, and insist that your Emperor stop what he would call illegal trade!' she went on, ignoring Mr Hartwell's interruption.

'Insist?' 'Mr Smith' raised quizzical eyebrows. '*Insist?* A little Corsican corporal insist that the Emperor of All the Russias do something? Anyone in Russia could tell you what the result of that would be! Alexander would use his greatest political talent. In fact, he would be sufficiently affronted to exercise it with more diligence and application that ever before!'

'And what is his greatest talent?' Caroline enquired, smiling in response to the lively, humorous expression on 'Mr Smith's' face.

'Masterly inactivity!' he replied. 'Unfortunately for your country, he'll probably exercise it towards England as well, but at least you'll get your masts and your ropes to keep your ships at sea, and Bonaparte's locked up in harbour, and who knows! One day Bonaparte may go too far and irritate our beloved Emperor into doing something, and then—why, *splat*! One squashed Corsican!' He laughed so merrily that the others joined in.

Suddenly he was serious again, and asked, 'Gentlemen, would you permit me a few words in private with Miss Barnes?'

Lord Cressing and Mr Hartwell looked at one another, appearing a little disconcerted, and then stood up, murmuring polite, 'By all means . . .' 'As you wish, sir . . .' and so on.

'There is no need to go out of the room,' 'Mr Smith' added with a smile. 'If you would discuss the weather over there by the sideboard for a minute or two, it would be sufficient.'

They withdrew the required distance, and 'Mr Smith' leaned towards Caroline, saying quietly, 'I gather that you are not sure that Mr Hartwell is to be trusted, which is sad for him, as he hopes to marry you. Perhaps I can help you?'

Caroline looked into his twinkling eyes, her own wide and solemn, and saw something rather sad and very compassionate in their emerald depths. She nodded.

'I had never met him before tonight, and yet I trust him!' he went on. 'In fact, I trust him with my life! That's partly because others whom I trust tell me he's honest and reliable, and partly my own judgment. Do you wish to trust him?'

'Yes!' Caroline breathed, knowing that she did, very much.

'Then do! Trust your own judgment of him, and the word of his friend. I'll show you . . . They,' nodding towards the two Englishmen, who were talking quietly at the far end of the room, 'tell me you are trustworthy, so I'll tell you something they don't know! My real name is Vassily Karachev, and I trust you not to tell anyone, not even Mr Hartwell!'

'Thank you!' Caroline whispered, feeling greatly complimented.

'And I'll give you something to prove that I come from Russia.' He felt in his pocket, produced a few coins and sorted through them, selecting one. 'There—a silver ten-kopek piece with this year's date!'

Caroline took it gratefully, and resolved to herself

that, if ever she felt inclined again to suspect Mr Hartwell of villainy, she would take out this silver whatever-
it-was and use it to remind herself not to be so fanciful!
She did not, however, forget to look at it, tilting it
towards the candles to see the details of it more clearly.
She recognised the double-headed eagle on one side,
and the date was right, but the inscription was in strange
letters, which she assumed were Russian.

She looked up and found that 'Mr Smith' was watching her with amusement. 'By all means, check the
available facts,' he said agreeably, and she felt her
colour rise a little, but she laughed with him.

'Thank you for your indulgence, gentlemen,' he called
across to the others, and they returned to their places.
But Lord Cressing consulted his watch and said, 'I think
we should be on our way. It will soon be daylight. Are
the horses ready, Robert?'

They all went together to the stable-yard, passing
through the silent house like a quartet of candlelit
ghosts, and it was not until they were outside that
Caroline murmured, 'I'd always assumed that Russians
would be dark-haired.'

'Some are fair,' 'Mr Smith' replied, 'in the Nordic
fashion. My mother was of Scottish descent. Does the
date of 1745 convey anything to you?'

'Bonnie Prince Charlie,' Caroline replied promptly,
and thereby publicly labelled herself a Romantic.

There were no horses in the stable-yard, and Mr
Hartwell did not appear to expect there to be any, for he
led the way across it and out into a small paddock, well
hedged round, where two mounts waited out of earshot
of the house, already saddled and bridled, and snug
under their blankets.

'Thank you for your hospitality,' said 'Mr Smith',
shaking hands with Mr Hartwell. 'I hope we may—er
—do business again some day, preferably from the same

side of—er—the same side of what?'

'The fence,' supplied Mr Hartwell. *'Bon voyage.'*

'Mr Smith' took both Caroline's hands in his own warm clasp and kissed them with more fervour than convention decreed, wishing her every happiness, which she thought a little odd, sounding as if she was about to be married, but she put it down to his being foreign, and wished him an eventual safe journey home.

He mounted with the easy grace which so much a part of all his movements, and rode off with Lord Cressing, leaving Caroline and Mr Hartwell to return to the house.

'Are you satisfied now?' he asked, sounding interested, but not sarcastic or annoyed.

'Yes, thank you. Oh, but I *must* apologise! I've thought the most terrible things about you, all without any justification at all! You must think me a complete ninny-hammer, to let my imagination run away with me like that!'

'My dear girl, I think nothing of the kind! I wrested you from the bosom of your very respectable and conventional family and brought you to just the sort of ancient, decrepit ruin which should be the setting for ghoulish and horrific happenings! You find here a young and lovely female kept prisoner by her wicked half-brother —and I'm aware that Julia can tell a fine tale when she's given half a chance. Said wicked half-brother then takes to making mysterious disappearances, for which he fails to provide a convincing explanation, and, when he *is* in residence, receives strange visitors by way of the library window in the middle of the night! In addition to all that, there's much talk of spies in the neighbourhood, where activities interesting to such characters are carried out in all directions, and then there are smugglers who make veiled allusions to red parcels—I take it that you now understand that one? I told Will he would recognise the right man by his hair.'

'Yes, I guessed that,' Caroline was glad to be able to reply, for it showed that she had not completely lost her wits.

'Even I, knowing what was really going on, can quite understand why you found it all somewhat confusing and sinister. In fact, when I think about it, I'm half inclined to suspect myself of something nefarious!'

'Oh, don't!' Caroline exclaimed. 'I shall assume in future that there's really a simple explanation for everything. And your house is *not* an ancient, decrepit ruin! It's a fine and beautiful house . . .'

'Apart from the dining-room,' he interpolated.

'. . . apart from the dining-room,' Caroline agreed. 'And I'm sure your ghost is a most *agreeable*, kindly old soul who would not frighten the most *timid* person, and your cellars are filled with fine wines and vats of cider, and not a single coffin or chained skeleton anywhere in them!'

At that moment, a small ghostly shape glided across the stableyard between them and the house, uttering a weird, unearthly cry. Mr Hartwell made a curious choking sound which Caroline suspected had started life as a shout of laughter, hastily stifled.

'That was an owl!' she said severely.

'Dearest Caroline!' he said, and drew her into an unexpected embrace, from which she did not attempt to escape, but leaned comfortably against him, thinking that Julia attached 'dearest' to the name of anyone for whom she felt affection, however slight, with a facile ease which totally devalued the adjective. But Mr Hartwell used it rarely, and in a very different tone of voice.

'Will you forgive me for thinking you a villain?' she asked a little gruffly.

'With all my heart, and we'll never mention the matter again!'

'Yes, all right,' Caroline said agreeably, making some

slight effort to move away from him, thinking it hardly proper to be caught by an early-rising servant enfolded in Master's arms in the middle of the stable-yard.

He let her go without comment, and walked with her back to her room, leaving her at the door with a kiss on her hand and a murmured, 'Sleep well, my dear, for what little time is left before morning. I'm sorry you've had such a disturbed night.'

Caroline was almost inclined to fall on to her bed as she was, for she suddenly felt very tired indeed, but she made the effort to undress and fold her clothes properly, as she always did, and then stretched out luxuriously between the cool sheets, thinking that she would be fit for nothing tomorrow, even if she managed two or three hours' sleep.

'But I don't suppose I shall have even that,' she thought. 'There's so much to think about and remember . . .' She turned on her side, snuggled her cheek into the pillow, and closed her eyes.

When she opened them again, the room was full of daylight, and Martha was putting out a fresh frock for her with a look on her face which said quite clearly that it was none of her business if her temporary mistress chose to get up and dress and go gallivanting in the middle of the night, *but* . . .

Caroline, feeling perfectly fresh and rested and free from care, bade her a cheerful 'Good morning,' but, of course, said not a word about the events of the night, which by now had assumed a slight air of unreality.

CHAPTER
FOURTEEN

JULIA'S EXPECTATIONS of receiving an immediate proposal of marriage were somewhat dashed the next morning when she returned with her brother and cousin from church to find a note awaiting her from the gallant Major.

'Oh, dear!' she exclaimed when she had read it. 'Dearest James says he has taken a few days' leave to visit his father, but hopes to wait upon me as soon as he returns.'

She sounded so puzzled and disappointed that Caroline realised that the poor girl probably had not understood that a young man of good family was no more able to propose marriage without his family's approval than was the object of his affections to accept without that of her own.

'He has to seek his father's consent, you know,' she said quietly.

Julia looked at her doubtfully, so she continued, 'There are legal matters to be decided—marriage settlements and so forth. It could prove very awkward if he entered into an engagement, and then his father disapproved and refused to allow him any money.'

She glanced at Mr Hartwell as she spoke, wondering if he would be able to put up the amount of dowry which no doubt Major Bridges's family would expect, but he was engaged in a lecture to Horatio on the iniquity of making toothmarks in the new pair of boots he was wearing, which had just been attacked according to custom.

Julia accepted Caroline's statement, and was reconciled to waiting, comforting herself, as she tactlessly remarked aloud, with the thought that Robert had been surprisingly good about the Major, and had not put her to the necessity of . . . She broke off before she had actually said 'eloping', but the guilty look which she gave Caroline was quite sufficient to make her sure that Mr Hartwell's story of the attempted elopement with Sir Charles Corbin was true after all, and she warmed a little more towards him in consequence.

Major Bridges had not returned by Tuesday—indeed, it was hardly reasonable to expect that he might, but Julia's virtues did not include patience, and she was becoming more than a little irritable and inclined to fall out with Mr Hartwell over nothing in particular. So Caroline should have been pleased to hear him say that he would be off on business in the morning, and could not say how long he would be away, but, although she was relieved that there would be less acrimony in the house, she had also to admit to a certain melancholy at the thought of not seeing his calm face or hearing his ironic tones for perhaps the rest of the week.

He left the house very early, as usual, and she resigned herself to a couple of days of trying to keep Julia busy and amused, for the alternative would be to have her mooning about the place, snapping at the servants and bewailing the intolerable length of dearest James's absence. She suggested that Julia might like to try her hand at painting, and brought down her own paintbox for the experiment.

'But what shall I paint?' Julia enquired, brush in hand and a pristine sheet of best paper before her, as blank, apparently, as her mind.

'Try this vase of flowers,' Caroline suggested, bringing a handsome floral arrangement from a console table and setting it before Julia.

The result was a colourful collection of splodges, but Julia, surprisingly, had become interested in the different forms and colours of the individual blooms, and took another sheet of paper, on which she made a fair attempt at some portraits of single flowers.

'These garden flowers are too gaudy,' she announced. 'I think I should like to try some small, delicate wild flowers. Shall we take a walk, Cousin Caro, and gather flowers in the hedgerows?'

Caroline concealed her amazement, and agreed that it would be pleasant to go flower-gathering. After luncheon, therefore, the two cousins went out, squired by Horatio, to see what they could find, going along a green lane which ran from the foot of the ridge towards the rising ground of the Forest.

'I hope it may not rain,' Caroline observed, for the sky was overcast, but Julia replied dismissively that it was nothing but a little cloud which would clear directly, and began to potter about in the hedge-bottom to see what she could find to lay in the trug which she had brought for the purpose. She looked a little incongruous in a green velvet pelisse with a bonnet to match, adorned with two large pale green ostrich plumes. Horatio, assuming that she was looking for rats like any sensible person, went to assist her by getting down into the dry ditch and snuffling about in likely holes.

Caroline idled about, occasionally picking an odd scabious or a trail of late honeysuckle, but with her thoughts far away. Only a few minutes before they came out, she had received a letter from her father, the contents of which had startled her considerably, but she had managed to scan them only hurriedly, as Julia was calling her. She was now longing for an opportunity to go away somewhere by herself and consider calmly and quietly what Mr Barnes had written.

He had begun with a brief summary of family news,

(the letter was dated the previous Saturday), but then had continued,

> I had a visit from Robert Hartwell this morning. He makes a very generous offer for you, in that he says that he sees no need for anything from me, but will make a settlement on you of two thousand a year during his lifetime, and five thousand a year if he should predecease you, and he produced evidence that he can do so without trouble. It appears that he inherited a considerable fortune of his own through his mother. I thought him to be an agreeable man, and likely to make a good husband, but you, of course, must make your own decision about that! If you take him, you'll have my blessing, but if you prefer to refuse him—well, there are other fish in the sea, and I cannot imagine that Miss Barnes, with her mother's looks and her father's fortune, will ever be hard put to find a husband.

Caroline hardly knew what to think. She was astounded to hear that Mr Hartwell was actually a very wealthy man, and, far from seeing her father about a loan, he had gone to offer for her hand in marriage! It was mortifying to think that she had nerved herself to mention the unmentionable to him in a charitable impulse to help him with his financial problems, when in fact he had none. How he must have laughed at her!

But where had she received the impression that he was hard-pressed? Why—from Mr Bell! Well, she would certainly set the gentleman right when she next saw him. How dare he spread tales about another man which could so damage his standing! He had even caused her to suspect Mr Hartwell of planning to marry her for money!

As her mind was occupied with these thoughts, she wandered along the lane and round a bend in it, while

Julia, who had found a clump of very pretty toadflax, remained some way behind trying to dig it up in one piece with a pair of nail-scissors from her reticule. Horatio progressed along the ditch, his passage marked only by sniffs and the slight agitation of the plants above his head.

There was a gateway in the hedge a short way past the bend, and Caroline vaguely noticed a horse and cart standing in the field just inside it, but, if she thought about it at all, it was only to assume that it was there for some agricultural purpose. She completely failed to notice the two men who were standing by it, let alone that they looked at one another as she passed as if they could hardly believe their luck, and moved out into the lane, following her.

A few spots of rain fell, startling her as one touched her face, and she looked up at the sky, which was now very threatening, but even as she did so, she was seized from behind in a rough grasp, and a growling voice said, 'Keep quiet and still, and you'll not get 'urt!'

Caroline's response to that was to scream in a brief and business-like fashion, and kick back against her captor's legs, making him yelp something which was not normally heard by young ladies. A hand clamped over her mouth, and a loop of rope was quickly passed round her body, pinning her arms, and then another round her ankles, causing her to overbalance and fall to the ground, wrenching herself out of her captor's hands.

As she fell, Julia came round the bend in the lane, stopped dead at the spectacle before her, and cried, 'Oh, Caro! What is it? Are they robbers?'

'Oh, Gawd! It's the other un!' exclaimed one of the men. 'Now what do we do?'

'Take 'em both!' the other man replied briskly. 'Grab 'er, quick!'

Julia turned to run, but the larger of the men was after

her, and had seized her before she had gone a dozen yards. Meanwhile, Horatio rose from the ditch like an avenging fate and sped to Caroline's rescue, but she called sharply, '*Home, Horatio! Go home! Fetch Master!*'

Horatio stopped in his tracks and looked at her in a puzzled fashion. The smaller man made a grab for him, but the dog bit his fingers *en passant* as he dodged, and the man clamped his injured hand under his other arm and swore, aiming a vicious kick at Horatio, who dodged again and looked enquiringly at Caroline.

'*Home, Horatio!*' she repeated desperately, fearing that the men would kill the dog if they caught him.

Horatio gave her a hard stare, then turned and bolted for home, easily evading and outdistancing his pursuer, who gave up the chase and turned his attention to helping his mate to tie Julia up as he had already tied Caroline.

'Be careful! You're dripping blood on my frock!' Julia said with some asperity. 'I don't know what you think you're about, but you'll be very sorry for it!'

'Not 'arf as sorry as you'll be if yer don't mum yer dubber!' one man replied threateningly. His words were unfamiliar to Julia, but his meaning was clear enough, as was the threat behind it, and she took the hint, but the larger man produced an old piece of fairly clean sheeting, tore it in half, and gagged both the young ladies, then helped the other to truss them and carry them one by one to the cart, where they were bundled in without much care, and covered with some empty sacks.

As the cart started off with a jerk, turned into the lane and went off rather too fast for comfort or safety on the rutted surface, Caroline tried her hardest to free herself, but the ropes about her wrists and ankles were securely tied, and she succeeded only in chafing her wrists until the touch of the rope was very painful. To judge by the heaving and grunting beside her, Julia was doing much the same, apparently with similar results.

After a time, the sounds of the horse's hoofs and the wheels of the cart changed, and they went for some distance on a metalled road, but Caroline could not judge how far they travelled or how much time elapsed. She only knew that it was raining heavily. The sacks which covered her were soon soaked, and chilly trickles of water began to find their way inside her clothing.

Eventually, the sounds of hoofs and wheels changed again as the cart turned off into a side lane, and again into a short gravelled drive, and then stopped. The sacks were flung aside, and she and Julia were picked up, one by each man, like sacks of merchandise, and she caught only a glimpse of a stable-yard before they were taken into what appeared to be a substantial house.

At first she could make little of it, for they were taken along a dark passage, but then the man carrying her stopped, opened a door, and entered a dark room, where he dumped her unceremoniously into a chair, and lit a candle in a stick which was standing on a nearby table. Julia was put down in another chair, across the room.

'I'll loosen yer gag, but 'sno use ter bawl, 'cos there ain't nobody to 'ear yer,' the larger man said.

Clumsy fingers pulled at the gag and got it off, and then her wrists were untied, but only that they might be refastened behind the chair, and finally her ankles were freed, and the other man served Julia in the same way.

'Nah, jest sit quiet and wait! Master'll be 'ome afore long!' the growling voice adjured them. Its owner pinched out the candle, then both men went out and shut the door. Almost immediately, it opened again, and the same voice said, 'There's bars acrost the winder, so yer won't get aht if yer frees yerselves!' The door shut again, and heavy footsteps receded down the passage.

'Caro? Dearest Caro? Are you all right?' Julia asked tremulously.

'Yes. Are you?'

'My wrists hurt, and my bonnet was dragged off and left lying in that horrid muddy lane!' Julia replied indignantly. 'What on earth is this all about? Have we been abducted, do you suppose?'

'I should imagine so,' Caroline replied. 'Presumably for ransom, although it all seems very strange. Those two men made no attempt to hide their faces, and I'm sure I'd recognise them both again!'

'Is abduction a hanging offence?' Julia asked with commendable calm, for she managed to sound as if she were enquiring if an ostrich were a bird.

'I believe so,' Caroline replied after a moment's thought, 'or at least, transportable . . .'

Conversation was, under the circumstances, somewhat desultory, and Caroline spent the intervals between remarks trying to find a reason for their abduction, but without any success. She was thankful that Julia seemed to have a good command over herself, and was not giving way to hysterics.

After what seemed an age, the heavy footsteps returned, the door opened, and the two ruffians reentered, this time with a branch of candles. The ropes were untied after warnings not to 'try anything', and the two ladies were half-pushed, half-dragged along the passage, further into the house, and arrived in a large room, dimly lit by a twelve-branch candelabrum on a tall stand.

The branch carried by one of their captors was put down on a table, and improved the light enough for Caroline to be able to see a little more of the room. Her eyes darted about, while her hands were busy trying to tidy her hair, which had come down when her bonnet was pulled off in the struggle back in the lane.

There were three doors—the one by which they had entered, one in the corner on the same side of the room, and another in the middle of the opposite wall, which looked like the front door of the house, for it was fitted with bolts, and there was a curtained window on either side of it. There was also a large key in the lock. The furnishings were simple—just three or four plain wooden chairs, one high-backed settle by the fireplace between the two internal doors, where a miserable fire smouldered, and a rectangular table, with another chair set midway along the far side of it. There was another small table over by the wall, on which stood a bottle and some glasses.

A man emerged from the shadows after a couple of seconds, but Caroline was not sure whether he had slipped in by the door in the corner, or had been standing by it observing them. It was not until he dropped his riding-crop on the table and sat down in the chair, facing her across it, that she recognised him.

'Mr Bell!' she exclaimed angrily. 'Why, what is the meaning of this?'

Almost simultaneously Julia exclaimed also, but she said, 'Charles! Good Heavens!'

'What the devil is she doing here?' the supposed Mr Bell asked irritably, glaring at Julia, but addressing the question to the two men. 'I told you to bring the one with the long hair!'

'Well, we did, and thought ourselves lucky to guess right where she'd be going the first time orf! 'Ow were we ter know the other was wiv 'er? She were round the corner, aht of sight,' the smaller man said defensively. 'We couldn't leave 'er to rise the alarm, so we brung 'em both.'

'You incompetent idiots!' Mr Bell said impatiently. 'Oh—get out! Go and tell that slut in the kitchen to prepare dinner—I'm famished!' The two men shuffled out, and Caroline took a step forward.

'We require an explanation of this infamous conduct!' she said sharply.

'Yes, Charles! What do you think you're about?' Julia demanded. 'Why did Miss Barnes address you as Mr Bell?'

'I take it that this is Sir Charles Corbin?' Caroline enquired of her cousin, and succeeded in making the 'this' sound as if she referred to a slug.

'Indeed, dearest Caroline!' Sir Charles replied with exaggerated sweetness, 'Your future husband, my dear!'

'What!' Caroline exclaimed, and Julia added, 'Are you run mad?' for good measure.

'Julia, sit down over there, and keep your mouth shut or I'll gag you!' Sir Charles said irritably, pointing to a chair over by the candlestand. 'Now, let me make myself plain. My income isn't sufficient for my needs, and never has been, and I've no mind to spend the rest of my life in the Marshalsea. A rich marriage is the answer. I thought I had dear little Julia's dowry as good as in my pocket, but her damned brother put paid to that! I meant to have another stab at getting her away, but while I've been lurking about here, I've hit on a better plan. I know how Cits fear scandal, particularly about their womenfolk, so I'll make sure the family will be as keen for the marriage as I am, and screw a good sum of the ready out of old Barnes—he'll be more susceptible to persuasion than Hartwell!'

'My father will never agree . . .' Caroline began, but Sir Charles interrupted with a scornful laugh.

'Oh yes, he will! After tonight, he'll be begging me to marry you, and offering ready money for it! Why, he'll pay anyone to marry you by the time I've finished enjoying your charms, my dear! It may take my two uncouth scoundrels to hold you down—they'll enjoy that—but you'll have lost your virtue by morning, believe me. Think yourself lucky that at least you'll be marrying a Baronet, and I'll not trouble you much once the money's paid over and the knot tied—in that order! You're not to my taste.'

It was the cold cruelty in his voice which made Caroline shiver, for it took a few moments for the meaning of what he had said to sink in, and then she thought she was about to faint, but she summoned her courage and forced herself to try to think.

'My brother will kill you,' Julia said quietly, the promise sounding the more convincing because she spoke in a controlled manner.

'The high and mighty Robert Hartwell don't deal in second-hand goods, and I bade you be silent!' Sir Charles said carelessly, lolling back in his chair. 'Don't remind me of your presence, or I may decide to have both of you tonight, and take the highest bidder in the marriage stakes. There's nothing like a little competition to raise the price!'

There was a shocked silence as both Caroline and Julia digested his meaning. It was Julia who recovered first, and said, in what sounded even to Caroline quite like her usual inconsequential manner, 'You do talk nonsense, Charles, and what on earth have you done to your hair? It don't suit you at all that colour!'

'Bleached it,' Sir Charles replied tersely. 'And I'm not talking nonsense. Now keep your mouth shut!'

Julia murmured something about ungentlemanly conduct, but then remained silent, for she had already had quite enough of being gagged. Caroline considered several things she might say—some of them likely to prove unwise, in the circumstances, then also decided to remain silent.

'No answer to it, is there?' Sir Charles remarked jeeringly. 'Well, now—let's see what I've caught. Take your pelisse off, girl!' As he spoke, his hand slid meaningfully across the table to touch the riding-crop, so Caroline thought it best to obey.

'Hm—still can't judge your figure,' Sir Charles commented, eyeing her up and down. 'Take the frock off as well.'

Caroline stared mutinously, but he picked up the crop and slapped it across the palm of his hand, then looked very deliberately at Julia. Caroline took his meaning, and removed her frock, folding it neatly and laying it on a chair, as if there was nothing unusual in being made to disrobe in front of a comparative stranger. She was thankful that her mother believed in substantial undershifts, not the more usual flimsy variety.

Sir Charles looked her over, and was kind enough to comment, 'Not as well-rounded as I usually like 'em, but I suppose I can put up with that, as long as your dowry's a good plump one! Pour me a glass of wine!'

Caroline walked slowly over to the small table where the bottle and glasses stood, her mind working feverishly. She glanced towards the front door, and tried to make out if the bolts were drawn or shot, but the light was too dim to see. There was an assortment of glasses on the table, so she filled a tumbler with wine, and carefully carried it to Sir Charles, going deliberately to the side of the table opposite where he was sitting.

'I see you're going to prove an amenable wife!' he said, smiling unpleasantly. 'I trust you'll be as prompt to serve me in bed as you are at table. Don't stand there staring—give me the wine!'

Caroline did—full in the face, and threw the glass at him for good measure, catching him a sharp blow on the temple which half-stunned him. She then seized the edge of the table and heaved it over on to him, sending the candles flying, and while he was wrestling with the recalcitrance of inanimate objects, she turned and ran for the front door. Julia, who could move surprisingly quickly for a lazy person, flung over the candlestand and arrived alongside her at the door as she seized the key and wrenched the door open, the bolts, fortunately, being drawn.

In a moment, they were both outside. Caroline said urgently, 'You go that way—we must split up!' and pushed Julia with one hand as she paused to lock the door on the racket which had broken out inside the house. Then she turned and ran the opposite way to that which Julia had taken, flinging the key away as she went.

It was pitch dark, and the rain was still teeming down. The front of the house opened directly on to a narrow road which seemed to be thickly bordered with trees. At first Caroline followed the road, trying to get as far as possible from the house, but it was no more than a rough lane, and she tripped on the ruts and stones too often to go fast, so she turned aside and plunged into the trees.

She was already soaked through by the rain, and could not see where she was going in the darkness, but the trees seemed to be continuous, not just a belt beside the road. She suddenly recalled that Miss Enstone had once said something about 'Mr Bell' having taken a house in the Forest, and realised at last roughly where she was. If she could keep going downhill, she would come eventually to the edge of the trees, and could then find her way to Woodham, or perhaps to Pinnacles, or even Canons Grange. At worst, if she was going east instead of west, she would come to whatever lay on the other side of the Forest, which, she recalled, was not above two or three miles wide.

Bushes and brambles caught at her clothing, and at times were so thick that she had to push her way through them, scratching her arms painfully. Twice, the ground seemed to fall away before her feet, and she went sprawling down a steep drop.

Always she was listening for sounds of pursuit.

Several times, she thought she heard voices shouting, and turned away from them, tripping over roots, bumping into trunks, falling over the unevenness of the ground, but still trying to go downhill, wondering desperately how far she must go to the edge of the Forest.

After what seemed to be hours, she stopped, crouching under a bush, thinking she could not go on much longer. She was shivering with cold and fright, bruised and scraped from her many falls, and so tired and confused that she hardly knew whether she was going up or down the slope of the ground. Again she thought she could hear voices, but they seemed like something in a nightmare now, and she wondered if she was imagining them.

'People die of being cold and wet and lost. I shall die if I stay here, and I'll never see Robert again . . .' Somehow, the thought of that was worse than the thought of dying, or even of being caught by Sir Charles Corbin, so she got to her feet again and stumbled on.

Presently she heard voices, closer this time, and certainly not imaginary, and there were sounds as if people were pushing through the undergrowth. The noises broke through her exhaustion, and spurred her to turn away and run full tilt down a shallow incline which seemed to be clear of trees, and then, suddenly, she came up hard against a dark shape, which though apparently braced to receive her, yielded slightly with a grunt at the impact, and then a pair of strong arms closed round her like a trap. She gave a sob of despair to think that, after all that she had gone through in her frantic flight, it had ended with her running straight back into the clutches of her captor.

'I always hoped you'd come to my arms at last,' a familiar voice remarked above her head, as the arms which were clasping her loosened and enveloped her in the voluminous cloak which their owner was wearing, and then pressed her more closely against his warm body. 'My poor dear! You're frozen with cold!'

'Robert?' she gasped.

'Yes, my dear. Shall we go home?'

'Oh, but Julia . . .'

'Is safe and well. She came running down the road nigh on two hours ago, straight into Bridges's arms, and told us all about it.'

Caroline gave a sob of relief, which developed into a short burst of crying, and then lapsed into a semiconscious state in which she felt only an enormous sense of relief, of being in the one truly safe place in the world. She was vaguely aware of voices calling that she was found to the searchers who had been beating their way through the Forest looking for her, but she did not become fully conscious again until gentle hands lifted her up to sit before Mr Hartwell on his horse, where she snuggled into his warm cloak, tucking her head into the angle of his neck and shoulder.

'Bridges took Julia home,' he said as he set his mount to a brisk trot along the lane in which he had been standing when Caroline came running out of the trees. 'We went up to the house to look for some sign of you there, but the place was deserted, save for a servant. Apparently Corbin and his henchmen had realised the game was up, and decamped.'

'How did you know what had happened?' Caroline asked sleepily. 'I thought you'd gone away.'

'There was some confusion over the arrangements, and I met the man I was going to see on the road, coming to see me, so we settled our business in the nearest inn, and I came home again. I fell in with Bridges along the way, and he came with me, expecting to see Julia. But when we reached the Grange, there was Horatio in the stable-yard, barking murder, rape and thieves, and obviously trying to tell us stupid humans something important. Then Warrener arrived with a more intelligible report. He was lurking behind a hedge, doing something rabbity, and saw the whole episode of your capture, but he's a prudent man with six children, so he came for help instead of interfering. Unfortunately, he can't run as fast as Horatio.'

'How did you know where we'd been taken?'

'We didn't. Horatio followed the scent along the lane for some way, but by then it was raining heavily, and I suppose it was washed out. Warrener's lurcher took us a little further, enough to indicate that you had gone into the Forest, and all we could think to do then was to call out every available man to come and search. Until the daylight failed, we were looking for the horse's prints —he had an odd shoe—and after that—well, it seemed better to go on shouting your name, hoping you might hear and reply, than give up and go home. I was about to despair, when Julia came down the road like a Derby winner. We thought at first that Corbin must have caught you, but there was a sluttish girl—some sort of housekeeper—at the house, and she swore that they'd only searched for you for a short time, and then gathered their belongings in a panic, and left. Now, no more talking. You're exhausted, and all the rest can wait until tomorrow.'

The journey home did not take long, for Mr Hartwell's horse seemed to know the short cuts, even in the dark, and kept up a brisk pace all the way. The women of the household, who had already had the pleasure of receiving Julia, then took over, and Caroline was clucked and exclaimed over, taken to her room, given a hot bath, anointed with arnica, witch-hazel, and various other sovereign remedies for scratches and cuts, bandaged about the wrists, and tucked into bed with two hot bricks and a posset containing three eggs and an inordinate amount of brandy.

Not surprisingly, it was very late when she awoke the next morning, feeling, on the whole, not much the worse for her adventure, apart from the bruises and scratches. Martha, who was sitting guard in the room, informed her that Mr Hartwell said she was on no account to get up until Dr Roberts had been, She did, however, agree to leave her post long enough to fetch Caroline some breakfast, suggesting that perhaps a little toast and tea might be acceptable. Caroline replied vigorously that she could do with rather more than that, and in fact managed a considerable quantity of fried ham and two eggs before progressing to the tea and toast.

By then, Dr Roberts had arrived. He was a stout and sensible country doctor, who made no fuss about Caroline's injuries, but pronounced them uncomfortable but superficial, and, after listening gravely to her breathing, asked her to cough two or three times, then said he could see no reason why she should not get up whenever she liked, as she did not appear to have taken pleurisy or (delicately feeling her forehead) even so much as a fever.

When he had departed, Caroline got up and dressed, finding herself stiff and sore. Then she put her father's letter into her reticule and went downstairs, but there seemed to be nobody about, so she continued out on to the terrace and looked down the long slope of the garden, but that, too, appeared to be deserted.

She wandered along the path down which she had twice hastened to speak privately with Mr Hartwell, and sat down on the seat where he had told her of Sir Charles Corbin's attempt to elope with Julia, and thought with some anger of that man's duplicity and effrontery, and then, turning her mind to a more pleasant subject, she took out her father's letter and re-read it.

Somehow, after yesterday's adventure, it seemed to

require very little consideration. After the physical effort and the fear involved in her escape, her feelings at finding herself in Mr Hartwell's arms had left her in no doubt that she loved him, but she was not at all sure that he reciprocated her sentiments.

After all, there were a number of reasons why a man might decide to marry a particular female which had nothing to do with love. She felt, knowing her father's shrewdness, that she might safely exonerate Mr Hartwell of being after her money, but he had never given any sign of being particularly fond of her, apart from an occasional jocular remark which seemed, on reflection, to be more like a clumsy attempt at flirtation by a man unpractised in the art.

She put the letter away and stared across the garden, wondering what she should do if Mr Hartwell proposed, as it seemed quite likely that he intended to do, and then she became aware that, right over the other side of the garden among the rosebushes, Julia was deep in conversation with Major Bridges, and, as his arm was about her waist and her head very nearly on his shoulder, it seemed probable that they had come to an agreement. She sighed, envying them.

'Landscape with lovers,' Mr Hartwell's cool, ironic voice remarked from behind her. 'How do you do this morning, my dear? Dr Roberts tells me you are unharmed, but medical gentlemen are not infallible.'

'I'm quite well, thank you,' Caroline replied, 'apart from bruises, cuts and sore wrists. Julia appears to be in the best of health.'

'Yes. An outburst of sheer fury does wonders for the system!' He sat down beside her, took her hands and kissed the bandage about each wrist, then neatly replaced her hands in her lap. 'She told me this morning the full tale of yesterday's events, and I think it was only in the telling that she realised just what Corbin is and what precisely he intended, and she's completely cured of him, thank God!'

'I think she was cured anyway.' Caroline nodded meaningly towards the two dark heads leaning together beyond the rosery.

'There's always a lingering regret for one's first love, unless one's illusions are totally shattered,' Mr Hartwell replied impersonally. 'What should I do, Caroline? My instincts tell me to find the fellow and give him a good thrashing, then hand him over to justice, but common sense points out that—to be honest—he might well thrash me, for he's bigger than I am! In any case, if the matter comes to court, he and a well-twisted lawyer could do considerable harm to your reputation, and Julia's, with a few well-chosen half-truths and innuendoes.'

'Yes, I suppose so,' Caroline replied thoughtfully. 'After all, Julia did try to run off with him, and he could make something of the fact that I had two or three conversations with him when there was no one else about, despite his never having been introduced to me . . . I think perhaps it would be best to do nothing, for I doubt if he'll show his face in our vicinity again.'

'You're sure?' Mr Hartwell looked searchingly at her. 'He insulted and threatened you, and you were hurt and frightened. It seems hard he should get off scot free.'

'He's really not worth bothering about,' Caroline replied, 'save for the possibility that he might try something similar with another female, who might not be as lucky as Julia and I were. If he were prosecuted, though, he might be transported, or worse, and I'd not wish that on anyone . . . But no, he shan't get off scot free! I know what to do—I'll tell my father what happened, and also that he's heavily in debt, and I think that should be sufficient to ensure that he goes to the Marshalsea, without any danger to Julia's reputation, or mine. My father knows some very useful people, including the magistrate at Bow Street . . .'

'The Bow Street Runners! My estimable Caroline!' Mr Hartwell exclaimed in tones of strong approval and admiration. 'Will you marry me?'

'I—I beg your pardon?' Caroline replied. She had been led to expect a proposal, but the abruptness and lack of preliminaries made this one something of a shock.

'Have you not received a letter from your father?' he asked anxiously.

'Yes. It came yesterday.'

'Oh. Well, what do you think, then?'

'About what?' Caroline felt that every nerve in her body had suddenly been stretched like a harp-string, for somehow she must find out why, and yet she would not ask directly.

'Oh, the devil!' Mr Hartwell muttered, passing a hand over his hair and marring its customary neatness. 'Look—I'm no hand at this sort of thing! I've never proposed marriage before in my life, and I've no idea how to go about it! What should I say?'

He sounded so agitated, so unlike his normal calm self, that Caroline almost relented and gave way to the temptation to spell it out for him, but she felt in her heart that she would always regret it if she did. The all-important confession must come from him, of his own accord.

'You can hardly expect me to know the usual form,' she said demurely. 'After all, I've never received a proposal of marriage before, apart from Sir Charles Corbin's unconventional version.'

'Then how does a young lady find out the proper way to respond, and so forth? Is it part of the esoteric lore passed on from mother to daughter? If it is, I can't imagine how Julia managed!'

'She reads novels of romance! They don't give an accurate picture of normal life, but they do set a certain standard of expectation that the romantic aspects of life should follow something of the established pattern contained in them.'

'I've never read a romance in my life!' Mr Hartwell sounded quite appalled. 'Am I to go away and read half a dozen in order to find out what I should say to you?'

Caroline was tempted to say 'Yes,' but she realised that this would condemn her to a considerable period of doubt and uncertainty, so she prudently replied, 'Well—briefly—it's usual for the actual proposal to be—er—preceded by—by an explanation . . .'

'Oh. Do you mean that I should tell you all the reasons why I think we should make a good married couple? I suppose I could begin by saying that Horatio's affection for you would cause him considerable distress if you ever went away from me, and you seem to have a considerable natural ability for organising things like, for instance, a Harvest Supper . . .'

'No, I don't mean that!' Caroline exclaimed hastily. 'It can be quite easily said in just a few words. Three, to be precise!'

There was a moment's silence, which seemed to Caroline to last for eternity, and she wondered desperately how long it would take him to work out her meaning. Surely he could not be so dull-witted that . . . Unless he had no deep feeling for her! Was he, after all, a man who considered marriage a matter of business, not of love? Struck by this horrid thought, she turned and looked at his face, and saw that he was watching her with a distinct twinkle in his eyes, and a smile lurking about his lips.

'Oh, you wretch!' she exclaimed. 'You know very well what I mean!'

'Dearest Caroline!' he said gently. 'I love you with all my heart! Will you marry me?'

She took a deep breath, preparatory to telling him what she thought of him for his teasing, for his arrogant assumption, for his playing upon her nerves in this way, and then said, 'Yes.'

He opened his arms, and she went into them with a sense of coming to her rightful and proper place, and lifted her face to his kisses. He seemed to know very well how to respond to that, despite his not having read the right books, and he soon had all her doubts and fears banished for good.

'I even disliked you to start with!' she exclaimed wonderingly between kisses.

'I know, and it nearly broke my heart! The moment I saw you, in your mother's parlour, I knew I must have you beside me for the rest of my life or never be happy again! Dearest, dearest Caro! I feared it might take years to win you, not just weeks, yet every day has seemed a year! I had no hope at all until—can you guess when I thought you might be beginning to like me a little?'

'When I ran out of the Forest into your arms?'

'No—before that. When you told me to borrow from your father, rather than from a banker! I know how carefully City folk avoid any mention of personal financial difficulties, and I thought that, if you could bring yourself to broach that subject with me, you must care for me a little.'

'Dear Robert!' she exclaimed, laughing, 'Do you know—I didn't have any idea that I meant to speak to you about it until I heard myself doing so, and then I came to the same conclusion that you did!'

The confession led to further kissing and murmuring, and kissing again, and this blissful state of affairs might have continued indefinitely, had not Horatio, coming round the corner of the house in pursuit of his own interests, caught sight of his beloved Caroline apparently in the process of again being assaulted by a man, and launched himself to the rescue, determined not to be sent away this time. He arrived in a confusion of yelps, barks, flying legs and ears, and teeth, which he sank smartly into the attacker's booted leg.

The result was chaos. Mr Hartwell uttered something of a bark himself and fell off the seat on top of the dog, almost pulling Caroline down with him. Simultaneously, Horatio's nose told him that he had made a mistake. He hastily withdrew his teeth and took instead to barking hysterically and wagging his whole body, let alone his tail, in his joy at finding Caroline alive, well, home again, and in a state of harmony with Master.

'Caroline,' Mr Hartwell said with restraint from a seated position on the gravel path, rubbing his offended leg with one hand, 'will you please take this dog of yours in hand and teach him not to attack my boots whenever he sees them!'

'But he's your dog!' Caroline protested.

'*With all my worldly goods I thee endow*,' Mr Hartwell replied. 'Starting with Horatio!'

Caroline laughingly leaned forward, not to help her affianced to his feet, but to pick up her newly-acquired dog and soothe him to silence and more seemly behaviour. Mr Hartwell picked himself up and resumed his seat at her side, and was presently able to continue the pleasant exchange of kisses and confidences with his beloved, albeit over the head of a shaggy white dog of indeterminate breed but distinctive character, which thumped both with his tail and added his own brand of kisses whenever opportunity offered.

To be read with caution whilst sunbathing.

The Mills & Boon Holiday Pack contains four specially selected romances from some of our top authors and can be extremely difficult to put down.

But take care, because long hours under the summer sun, engrossed in hot passion can amount to a lot of sunburn.

So the next time you are filling your suitcase with the all-important Mills & Boon Holiday Pack, take an extra bottle of After Sun Lotion.

Just in case.

PRICE £4.40 AVAILABLE FROM JUNE 1986